THE IMPOSSIBLE

COSMOS

Other books by Walt McLaughlin:

The Unexpected Trail
Taking on the 100 Mile Wilderness
(narrative)

Forest under my Fingernails
Reflections and Encounters on the Long Trail
(narrative)

The Allure of Deep Woods
Backpacking the Northville-Placid Trail
(narrative)

Arguing with the Wind
A Journey into the Alaskan Wilderness
(narrative)

A Little Crazy in Paris
(travel narrative)

Backcountry Excursions
Venturing into the Wild Regions of the Northeast
(short narratives)

Worldly Matters
(essays and short narratives)

Loon Wisdom
Sounding the Depths of Wildness
(essays and short narratives)

Nature and Existence
(philosophical essays)

A Hungry Happiness
(poetry)

THE IMPOSSIBLE COSMOS

A Year of Amateur Astronomy and Big Questions

by

Walt McLaughlin

Wood Thrush Books

Andromeda Galaxy shown on the front cover.
Cover image courtesy of Shutterstock.com

Published by Wood Thrush Books
85 Aldis Street
St. Albans, Vermont 05478

ISBN 978-0-9903343-3-0

To seekers everywhere,
of every stripe and color

Preface

On a clear night in the summer of 2003, I gazed upon Mars twinkling like any fixed star and thought about what it was exactly that I was seeing. Millions of miles stretch between that planet and the one upon which I stand, but this fact meant nothing to me at the time. All I knew was that the star shining before me was no star at all. Its location and faint orange hue assured me of that. I was looking at Mars. No big deal some would say, but the reality of what I was seeing struck me with full force: that's another world out there, similar to this world. And for a fleeting moment I understood how ridiculous this concept must have seemed to people living five hundred years ago.

A few months later I began my first serious foray into amateur astronomy, which is recounted here in great detail. In the year that followed, a combination of in-depth study and evening viewings took my mind places it had never been before. "Space is the place," the musician Sun Ra chanted during a jazz fest that I attended once, and now I believe it. One must turn to the night sky to understand the nature of our world and how it fits into the greater scheme of things.

I am no scientist by any stretch of the imagination. I remain a poet, mystic and philosopher even as I calibrate scientific instruments and unravel complex formulas. I am a woods wanderer who has perchance wandered deep into the cosmos. My interest in what's out there is ontological for the most part. I want only to better understand the difference between what is and what is not. For me the magnificence and beauty of the night sky is secondary. Nature with a capital "N" is what I'm after.

Having said that, there is no point denying simple scientific facts. Despite my religious and philosophical inclinations, I have become a firm believer in the scientific method. I see it as a vital tool in our collective quest for truth. To some people the fusion of reason and mysticism, of science and religion, only makes it more difficult to understand such things. Better to keep these matters in their nice, tidy boxes. But my ruminations through the years have taken me to a different place. When I look into the eyepiece of a telescope and see a galaxy swirling about there, I experience nothing less than an encounter with the divine.

I wrote the first draft of this book back in the fall of 2005 then set the manuscript aside. What was the point of finishing it? Since I have no scientific credentials, I figured that no publisher would touch something like this. More to the point, I couldn't promote this book effectively enough to cover printing costs even if I self-published it. Eight years later, I had a change of heart. By then on-demand printing had altered the publishing game enough to make self-publishing a lot more affordable. So I gave this manuscript a second look. I was pleasantly surprised by what I found there. As a result, I finished writing it in 2014.

Yes, there is plenty of science in this book, but it's really more about the long, winding road towards understanding – both the personal one that I undertook during that critical year, and the collective one that humankind has taken since the dawn of civilization. These are subjects that I feel comfortable writing about, being a lifelong wanderer as well as an avid student of history. As for my responses to the Big Questions that arise along the way, what can I say? My worldview is no crazier than anything else passing for philosophy or religion these days. So I hope that you, dear reader, will keep an open mind while reading this story. If nothing else, I'm sure that you'll be entertained by the journey.

Walt McLaughlin
December 2015

In the beginning God created the heavens and the earth.

– Genesis 1: 1

Which pattern had the artificer in view when he made the world – the pattern which is unchangeable, or that which is created?

– Plato

If you admit the existence of time before the creation, you will be compelled to accept the theory of the eternity of the universe.

– Moses Maimonides

Quantum Mechanics is very impressive… but I am convinced that God does not play dice.

– Albert Einstein

If the universe is really completely self-contained, having no boundary or edge, it would have neither beginning nor end: it would simply be. What place, then, for a creator?

– Stephen Hawking

THE IMPOSSIBLE
COSMOS

1

Sometimes reality is wilder than the wildest fantasy. Who is prepared for the simple facts that appear out of nowhere to shake our beliefs to their foundations? We live our lives as if the world makes perfect sense, as if the universe is simple, orderly, predictable, and unchanging. We have to do this in order to function on a daily basis. I'm certainly no exception. So when something like *this* is thrown in my face, I'm not sure what to think.

While channel surfing the television, I have stumbled upon a mild-mannered fellow giving a lecture on astrobiology. His presentation is rather flat and the camera seems to be fixed in place. If my wife were here, we would quickly change the channel. But left to my own devices this evening, I hesitate. The multi-colored, gaseous cloud projected onto the screen behind the man has caught my attention. So has that word: *astro*-biology. A caption at the bottom of the screen states that the gaseous cloud is such-and-such nebula, several thousand light-years away. The lecturer calmly informs his audience that, along with hydrogen, helium and other gasses that one would expect to find in a nebula like this, it also contains the building blocks of life: oxygen, carbon, water molecules – perhaps even life itself.

My initial reaction to this claim is a giggle that thinly masks profound skepticism. But the lecturer uses known physics, astronomy, and chemistry to make a strong and convincing case. Twenty minutes later, my head is reeling from the possibility of life forms, however primitive, just floating around out there in deep space. Okay, stop right there. This is too much to consider right now. It's a Thursday in the middle of November, and I've spent a whole day doing various kinds of literary work as I usually do this time of year. I'm tired. So I turn off the television, grab some light reading and head for bed. What occurs in some nebula light-years away is not my concern. All the same, I am haunted by the prospect of a strange and vital universe.

The next day begins with a round of writing, per usual. I haven't forgotten about that nebula but I push it into a dark corner of my mind so that I can get something done. Eight hours later, I pack up my things and head for the Ethan Allen Motel where I work as a front desk clerk on weekends. Along the way, I slip into a Barnes and Noble bookstore to look at astronomy magazines. For years I've been warning my wife Judy that I intend to take up astronomy as a hobby someday – probably in my old age. I've been playing around with cosmological ideas and gazing into the night sky for decades. It's just a matter of time before I get serious about it. I'm only in my forties now with many years ahead of me. Way too soon to get into all that. But why wait? The universe beckons. It taunts me with its riddles.

Since this is a big bookstore, there are several amateur astronomy magazines to choose from. I select one called *Skywatch '04* that contains a buyer's guide to telescopes and some interesting tips on stargazing as well as star charts for the coming year. Seems like a good place to start. I purchase it then go directly to work.

At the motel office late in the evening when all is quiet, I peruse the magazine, learning what I can about the various instruments used to probe the night sky. Refractors and reflectors, Dobsonian and Newtonian – they're all more complicated and expensive than I expected them to be, but not entirely beyond my reach. How big does a telescope have to be, I wonder, in order to see things like nebulas and galaxies? Clearly, I have much to learn about the matter. I'm a complete novice in this field. This is the beginning of a brand new adventure for me – similar in many ways to the first trips I took deep into wilderness areas in my youth. Only this time the wilderness is the universe at large.

A television show for chrissakes. Such a silly beginning. But great journeys begin sometimes with the most trivial and commonplace first steps. Now there's no stopping me. There are things I simply have to know about the world around me – things that can't be learned from books alone. As a general rule, I put more stock in ideas than appearances when it comes to learning, but direct encounter has its merits. Over the years I've used direct encounter to better understand the natural world. So I dream about seeing things as Galileo saw them four hundred years ago, as a few others living around me see them now. Seeing is believing.

Not too long ago, I read a book called *The Sacred Depths of Nature*, written by a cell biologist named Ursula Goodenough. In it she describes how life developed from the simple ingredients of a "primal soup" to self-aware creatures like our selves. Going back and rereading sections of that book, I find that she mentions the possibility that comets or meteors might have picked up "molecular building blocks" while passing through interstellar dust clouds then delivered them to Earth. Somehow I missed that during my first reading. I recall a similar claim made by the Russian biochemist A. I. Oparin in *Origin of Life*, published back in the 1930s. I read that book many years ago and remember laughing at the prospect of life being delivered here via meteorite. Now that idea isn't so funny.

There's a simple factoid in Ms. Goodenough's book that I've encountered before but still have difficulty grasping: There are roughly 100 billion galaxies in the universe, each with about 100 billion stars in them. My initial reaction to this is astonishment. Throw the word "infinite" at me and I'm okay, but really big numbers boggle my mind. They are *astronomical*, which is like saying *incomprehensible*. All the same, I take a few minutes to consider one of the glaring implications of that statement.

Are we the only intelligent life form in existence? Who could possibly hold such a belief in a universe so vast, when the building blocks of life can be generated in one of the many nebulas found in countless galaxies? "Mystery generates wonder," Ms. Goodenough writes in her book, "And wonder generates awe." Yeah, I guess so. I'm awestruck, that's for certain. The universe is a big place and surprising things are happening in it, no doubt.

A little over a year ago, I enjoyed an excellent view of the Milky Way on a clear, August night. I was deep in the West Canada Lakes Wilderness, located in the southwestern corner of the Adirondacks. There wasn't a cloud in the sky when the sun went down. No moon either as I recall. I sat with my dog on the lapping shores of a quiet lake with that black, star-filled dome stretched overhead. I saw thousands of stars, including a few "shooting stars" streaking across the sky. I saw fuzzy objects scattered throughout the Milky Way and wondered about them. I felt a powerful urge to know exactly what I was seeing and made a mental note to find out someday. Yeah, someday I would stop taking the night sky at face value and delve deeper into it. Well, it looks like that day has arrived. Now the urge has become irresistible.

A few days after that television show on astrobiology, Judy and I are browsing a bookstore as we usually do this time of year. It's almost Thanksgiving. Vermont has turned cold and we need more books to get us through the coming winter. Bargain hunter that I am, I have gravitated to the remainder tables in the back of the store. I find a hardcover in pristine condition called *The Universe at Midnight*, written by Ken Croswell and published only a couple years ago. I crack it open and soon fall upon a sentence that grabs me: "During the day, scientists and philosophers can construct elegant theories of how they think the universe should operate; but at night, at midnight, when powerful telescopes swing toward distant galaxies, the universe delivers its verdict." Being a philosopher of sorts, with my own theories about how the world is organized, this hits home. It also fuels the fire of my growing interest in astronomy. I shut the book, clenching my fist around its spine. This one is a keeper.

A few hours later, I have an *astronomical* moment before even finishing the first short chapter of that book. Croswell informs me that our Milky Way Galaxy is gravitationally bound to another large, spiral galaxy called Andromeda, along with three-dozen smaller galaxies, in what is known as the Local Group. That group is part of an even larger association of thousands of galaxies known as the Local Supercluster, which is part of an even larger cluster known as the Great Attractor. *Ka-boom!* My head explodes. I set the book aside, vowing to return to it when I am capable of dealing with what its author has just told me.

Is the universe one great big structure? If so, how did it get that way? What about the Big Bang? How does that factor into all this? What about chaos? I thought a random universe, ruled by quantum uncertainty, was the dominant scientific paradigm of our day. What about God? Has cosmology been stripped clean of God-talk once and for all, or is it more relevant now than ever before? Suddenly it occurs to me that it has been a long time since I last read a book on the cosmology. I'm out of touch. I'm confused by the snippets of information that have come my way lately, mostly from mainstream news reports. The ever-questioning philosopher within me is awakening. Once again I'm standing face-to-face with life's Big Questions, with stuff I thought I had resolved years ago. But scientific knowledge has grown by leaps and bounds during the past couple decades, and I have only a cursory understanding of such things. It's time to change that.

How can I explain this sudden urge to explore the stars, crack open the science books, and make sense of the world? The cosmos at large is far removed from pressing, day-to-day matters. Surely there are better, more practical ways to utilize one's time and energy. But I'm hooked now. The nature of the universe is essentially a philosophical matter, and I simply can't let go of the urge to know as much about it as possible.

In *The Sacred Depths of Nature* Ms. Goodenough frames this urge as well as anyone can: "To take the universe on – to ask Why Are Things As They Are? – is to generate the foundation for everything else." That is the driving force behind every quest for truth – not practicality, utility or relevance. A seeker longs for a solid foundation upon which to build his or her worldview. That is the driving force behind my sudden and compelling interest in astronomy, anyhow. As in the days of Copernicus, when a sun-centered cosmology challenged the medieval worldview, humankind now appears to be poised on the verge of a major breakthrough in understanding. I wish to be a part of that, instead of some witless advocate of simplistic beliefs seemingly rooted in common sense.

So I'm bracing myself for a wild ride. After all, cosmology isn't for the faint of heart.

2

Begin at the beginning. Before acquiring a telescope and turning it towards the stars, I first have to learn how to make my way around the night sky. There are thousands of stars out there visible to the naked eye on a clear night. To a novice like me, well, they all pretty much look the same. Boost up the magnification with a telescope or a pair of binoculars and the number of visible stars increases dramatically. In other words, it's a wilderness out there. I need to orient myself. I need a map.

The constellations were invented a long time ago to make sense of the night sky, to make it easier for stargazers like me to get around out there. Constellations are loose associations of stars that form a picture in one's mind when seen a certain way. Take Cassiopeia, for example. The major stars in it form a distinct "W" in the night sky. Other constellations form animals, common objects, mythological creatures, ancient Greek heroes, etc. Each civilization has had its own interpretation of the night sky, but modern astronomers have settled upon the Greco-Roman constellations. There are 88 constellations altogether. About two-thirds of them are visible on any given night.   To those of us living in the Northern Hemisphere, the other third are permanently below the southern horizon.   Tonight I'm venturing outside to learn a few of the constellations that I can see.

With a flashlight and a star chart in hand, I look up and identify a few of the more obvious constellations. First I spot The Little Dipper, which is only part of a larger constellation – what scientists call an asterism. The Little Dipper is in Ursa Minor, or the Little Bear, which is a little harder to see. The Big Dipper, in Ursa Major, isn't quite visible right now. It's half hidden by the trees on the northern horizon. Near the Little Dipper is Cassiopeia – that familiar "W." Further down the Milky Way is Cygnus, the Swan, which looks like a big cross to me. Almost directly overhead is the Great Square in the constellation Pegasus.   Wow!   How come I never noticed *that* before? The answer is quite simple. I haven't been looking for it.

As every stargazer soon learns, some stars are brighter than others. The brightest stars are easy to spot, naturally, so they make the constellations in which they're located easier to identify. The star, Deneb, marks the constellation Cygnus. Vega, one of the brightest stars, points out Lyra even though I can't see much of that constellation. Aldebaran queues me to the constellation Taurus, with a little help from my star chart, of course.   It's not as hard to learn the constellations as I thought it would be. The trick is to keep them all sorted out.

While studying the sky, I notice that the constellations are moving. The night sky is a giant wheel slowly turning around a single point known as the North Star, or Polaris. It appears to be moving east to west. That means that the constellations rising in the east just after dusk will eventually set in the west, just as the Sun does. The farther south one looks, the more the constellations seem to follow the path of the Sun as it moves across the sky during the course of a day. In fact, the Moon, the planets and the constellations of the Zodiac all travel along the Sun's path, give or take a few degrees. This path is called the *ecliptic*. No doubt the recognition of this common path was the beginning of both astronomy and astrology a long time ago. After identifying it, I have a better sense of the night sky and how easy it must have been for our ancestors to jump to conclusions. This is something worth pondering as I quit my stargazing and go back indoors where it's warmer.

"The night sky is the hunting ground of the mystic and the philosopher, the scientist and the theologian," Chet Raymo wrote in his book, *The Soul of the Night*. No doubt this was as true many thousand years ago as it is today. In a time when one could easily be a mystic, philosopher or theologian as well as a scientist, that hunting ground must have been irresistible. I see why the high priests of the emerging civilizations looked to the night sky for answers to life's great mysteries. There are definite patterns out there and the fact that those patterns are not easily discernable makes them even more alluring. Obviously those high priests had a lot of time on their hands otherwise they couldn't have been able to work out the complex movements of heavenly bodies. This much we can say for certain about ancient astronomy. We can also surmise that the practical aspects of stargazing probably ran a distant second to sheer curiosity in the very beginning. All the same, practicality must have soon become the driving force.

Records left behind by ancient Chinese stargazers indicate that they were observing the night sky as far back as the 24th century BC, perhaps longer. At first these observations were only used in oracles, but the desire to improve agriculture eventually led to the development of calendars. These calendars were based upon celestial events: the phases of the Moon, the vernal and autumnal equinoxes, the summer and winter solstices, etc. Since the constellations complete their trip around the North Star once a year (in addition to once a day), they played a significant role in determining time. No doubt they became even more important than the Sun and the Moon when it came to working out *annual* details. At any rate, the ancient Chinese made good use of the constellations, as did ancient Egyptians, Mayans, Indians of the Asian subcontinent, and other early agrarian civilizations. And they all had their own kind of astrology at one time or another. But the Babylonians were the ones who really ran with it.

We can trace the signs of the Zodiac to the days when the Babylonians ruled the Mesopotamian Valley. Babylonian astronomy goes back to at least 1800 BC. The Sumerians, who predate the Babylonians, probably had some sort of primitive astronomy before that. The Babylonians paid careful attention to the passage of the Sun, Moon, planets, and stars along the ecliptic. The signs of the Zodiac are all located on or near the ecliptic – that imaginary line that the Sun draws across the sky.

They believed that the movements of these celestial bodies determined the fate of human beings, giving them good reason to pay attention. Hence the birth of astrology as we know it today.

The beliefs of those who lived several thousand years ago still loom large in the night sky overhead. To this day, the constellations we see there, rooted in Babylonian astrology, still bear their Greco-Roman names: Aries, Taurus, Gemini, Virgo and so on. One would think that the constellations would have been revised by now, that their names would have been changed to better reflect the enlightened, scientific worldviews that we moderns now embrace. But that's simply not the case. We still make our way around the night sky the same way that ancient soothsayers did.

Towards the end of November, during my next excursion into the night sky, I take my binoculars with me. Is it true that some stars appear to have color, as field guides to the stars suggest? I'm about to find out. I'm still trying to learn the constellations, certainly, but now I'm on another mission as well. I've been doing some reading about stars lately so I wish to see them as something more than mere pinpoints of white light in the dark canopy overhead.

"The forgoing generations beheld God and nature face to face; we, through their eyes," Ralph Waldo Emerson wrote in his remarkable little book, *Nature*, "Why should not we also enjoy an original relation to the universe?" My sentiment exactly. It isn't enough to merely hear reports regarding celestial matters. I wish to see as much of it as possible with my own eyes.

Remarkably enough, it's true. Looking carefully through my binoculars, I can actually detect a slight yellow cast to Capella in the constellation Auriga. Aldebaran, the brightest star in Taurus, seems orange. Betelgeuse, just now rising above the eastern horizon, is a much darker orange. Some stars, like Deneb and Fomalhaut, are definitely white. Others, like Vega, have a barely discernable blue hue to them. Amazing. I had no idea that there was color of any sort in the night sky. But all I had to do was look.

What gives each of these stars their distinctive hue? Color is an indicator of heat intensity. Betelgeuse is a relatively cool red giant at 3,000 degrees centigrade, while Aldebaran is a slightly warmer orange star. Light yellow Vega, is a common, middle-of-the-road star like our Sun, burning at roughly 6,000 degrees on its surface. Truly white stars (as opposed to those that merely look white) are considerably warmer. The hottest stars like Vega are blue, with temperatures approaching 25,000 degrees. Now that's what I call hot. But we're talking only surface temperatures here. Stars are much hotter at their cores.

While hot stars burn brighter than cool ones, the apparent brightness of a star as seen from earth is no indication of its heat intensity. Much depends upon how far away the star is from us, how large it is and what we're actually seeing. Sirius is the brightest star in the night sky, but it's actually a white dwarf a mere eight and a half light years away from us. Betelgeuse, on the other hand, is a cool red giant about 640 light years away, but shines brightly because it's so big. In the last phase of its life, Betelgeuse has swollen to immense size – hundreds of millions of miles in diameter. Other bright stars, like Capella, are actually binary systems, meaning that they are actually two stars. Since those stars are locked together in a gravitational dance and thereby very close to each other, they appear to us as one star. Sometimes appearances are deceiving.

Even the closest stars are light years away. Light years – what a concept! We all know that a light year is the distance that light travels in a year (roughly 6 trillion miles), but who can really comprehend such a thing? I've done a little simple math in an attempt to make sense of the concept and this is what I've come up with: It takes about 8 hours for light to travel across our Solar System. Multiply that times three and you get one light day. Multiply that times 365 days and you get one light year. That means an object one light year away is roughly a thousand "solar-system lengths" away. That's as close as I can come to wrapping my brain around the idea.

The more I look and learn, the more it seems to me that space is a very strange place. Bellatrix, Altair, Mizar, Alcor – even the names of the stars seem strange to me. Where did all these strange names come from? Most of them have Greek origins, naturally, but many are Arabic. Some of the brightest stars are Arabic, in fact: Aldebaran, Betelgeuse, Deneb, Formalhaut, Rigel, Vega and others. These names only intensify the creeping sense of the otherworldly that I feel as my eyes wander about the night sky. It is not my world out there; it isn't even my language. Everything about it is unfamiliar.

The unfamiliarity of the night sky runs deeper than mere words. I have a strange new mindset these days, as well – one that runs counter to my formal training in the humanities, my countless frolics in deep woods, and my artistic/literary sensibilities. I am thinking *scientific* thoughts. But I'm a creative writer for chrissakes, not an exacting scientist. All this talk of heat, distance and size is more alien to me than the Greco-Arab names for it all. This reminds me of what Thoreau once wrote in his journals: "Every poet has trembled on the verge of science." Well, look who's trembling now.

As I lower my binoculars and go back indoors, though, I feel something I haven't felt in years. I feel intellectually exhilarated – something that only comes when one exposes oneself to new and different ways of thinking. I feel a deep sense of satisfaction, as well, having learned a great deal already. It has only been a week and a half since that astrobiology television show, yet I've learned more about the night sky during that time than I had during the previous three decades. Still a long way to go, certainly, before I have a good sense of what's out there, but the prospect is exciting. It is also a bit scary. Maybe this new knowledge will alter my sense of what is real and what isn't. Maybe it will change my worldview. We shall see.

3

Astronomy is more of an indoor activity than one might think. While I might go outside to look at the night sky a couple times a week, I have my nose in a book and am on my computer nearly every day. This study is essential. After all, the learning curve is steep in this science. There's much to know before the simplest observations can make any sense at all. Besides, you have to know where to look when you are surfing the stars. Space is a big place.

The Internet is an invaluable tool when it comes to learning any science. Punch the word "astronomy" into a search engine and a vast reservoir of knowledge suddenly opens up. But what I want to know is this: Where are the best pictures and the most easily accessible information? The answer varies according to personal taste, certainly, but I've quickly come to appreciate NASA's Astronomy Picture of the Day website. One can find more exciting visuals and more in-depth information elsewhere, but APOD is one of the most comprehensive websites out there. Just about everything related to space shows up on it at one time or another. And every day the people who manage it post something new.

Some of the pictures at the APOD website are incredible, especially those taken by the Hubble Telescope – that somewhat pricey instrument orbiting the earth well beyond all atmospheric hindrances. More than once I have clicked onto a page and gasped at the photograph before me. I'm particularly fond of the enhanced-color shots of nebulas and galaxies. I drool over them the way that other men drool over the airbrushed photos of naked, beautiful women in sex magazines. My wife is beginning to worry about me. Have I become just a tad too enthusiastic about my newfound hobby?

The more I learn, the more I see in those pictures. A galaxy is no longer a mere collection of stars. Now I see star-making nebulas full of chemically rich dust, blue giants populating long stellar arms that stretch into the void, and a mysterious core that most likely hides a black hole. The telltale shape and color of a galaxy speaks volumes about its nature and evolution – most of which I haven't fathomed yet so my imagination runs wild. The captions below the pictures at the APOD website inform me daily. I can't believe that we know as much as we do about the physical universe. I can't believe that scientists have learned as much as they have during the past few decades. Many pieces of the cosmic jigsaw puzzle have slipped into place since I was a kid.

When I was sixteen years old, I gazed upon the stars the same way that Babylonian soothsayers once did, looking for clues regarding the fate of humanity in general and myself in particular. It was a sketchy mix of wishful thinking, desperation and ignorance, with just a touch of madness to boot – just the kind of thing that keeps conscientious parents awake at night. By the time I was seventeen, though, I had come to my senses. Then I saw the stars as stars, as celestial bodies way off in the distance and quite independent from life here on earth. All the same, the night sky has remained a mysterious and wonderful place. Back then and ever since, the stars have filled me with awe.

Wonder and awe are immediate; wisdom comes slowly. I was taking a metaphysics course in college before I heard the word "cosmology" used in any meaningful way. Cosmology, along with ontology and epistemology, is simply a branch of metaphysics. The latter deal with existence and knowledge; the former deals with the physical universe – its structure and how it came to be. Not until I took that metaphysics course did it occur to me that human beings are *physically* connected to the universe at large. And cosmology is where the study of that connection begins.

The word "fate" indicates a poor understanding of the connection between humankind and the cosmos. It presumes a preordained series of events that the vastness of space itself undercuts. Cosmology is more about dynamics than inevitability. How does the universe operate? Is it one big system or a random series of events? Assuming that some kind of order exists in the universe, the question arises: What's the driving force behind that system? Take your pick. Some people say that the cosmic system is a rational one, thereby planting their worldview securely in the firmament of mathematics. Others call it "nature," allowing for a mystical variable or two. Still others use the word "God" when discussing such matters. From there things quickly get out of hand.

In the years following college, I picked up a few books on the origin and nature of the universe. These books were written by astronomers trying their best to make things like quasars, black holes, and the Big Bang theory intelligible to general readers like me. They were only partially successful. Whenever the numbers got too big for my brain to handle, or whenever the Theory of Relativity or Quantum Mechanics snuck into the discussion, my head exploded. It never failed. So I resigned myself to an imperfect understanding of such things and developed a worldview in accordance with more comfortable modes of thought. That is, I remained fundamentally religious and philosophical in my outlook – science be damned. But one cannot think this way indefinitely if one has a healthy respect for the truth. Eventually, science turns certain hypotheses into facts and one is compelled to face them. Either that or live a life of illusion.

I call myself a philosopher because I'm a lover of wisdom. I want to know everything that can be known about the world, even if that knowledge is painful. The degree in philosophy that I took away from Ohio University is beside the point. I had a great uncle who was a deep thinker despite the fact that his formal education never went beyond high school. His abiding desire to understand the world made him a philosopher. In other words, he cultivated an open-mindedness that would not deny truth when the evidence became overwhelming – even when the facts ran counter to what he wanted to believe. All bona fide philosophers are bound by their natures to accept things as they really are.

With this in mind, I have cultivated a worldview over the past few decades while trying to keep an eye on the scientific realities that are constantly emerging. This isn't easy to do and is not always pleasant. Seems like those realities are constantly forcing me to make adjustments to what I believe. Sometimes it seems like those realities get in the way of what I *want* to believe. But that's okay. It is better after all, to be constantly adjusting one's worldview than to embrace a credo that is delusional. That is, if one cares at all about the truth.

Science doesn't have all the answers. It never did and never will. Science takes place on the frontier of knowledge. By definition that's what it is. So we are forced to speculate, at any given point in time, about the true nature of things. There's no getting around this. As James Jeans wrote in his book, *Physics and Philosophy*: "Wherever science leaves off – and in many places its boundary is ill-defined – there philosophy begins." So I take my philosophizing quite seriously despite the many advances of science. I continue my pursuit of wisdom which, when all is said and done, comes down to venturing the best guesses possible about what is real.

It's early December. I bundle up then grab my binoculars, flashlight, and star chart before heading out the door. I hop in my car and drive into the dark countryside, escaping the glaring town lights that hide most of the stars. After parking my car along a rarely traveled dirt road, I tramp into the middle of a windblown, snow-covered farmer's field for a good look at the night sky. The light pollution from Montreal, about sixty miles away, creates a starless, blue dome to the northwest. That dome rises twenty degrees above the horizon but leaves the rest of the sky wide open to my hungry eyes. The Milky Way stretches across the sky, east to west – a great river of stars. The constellation Cygnus anchors the Milky Way in the west. Gemini, just now rising in the east, holds down the other end. The moon shines brightly in the center of the southern sky, obscuring many of the stars there. No matter. I'll work around it.

I do a quick inventory of the constellations that I know: Pegasus, Cassiopeia, Ursa Minor, Taurus and so forth. Then I identify a few more: Auriga, Cepheus and even Cetus in the south despite the moon. A frigid wind whips out of the west, freezing my face. I turn my back to it. What's that over there – that line of three stars just above the eastern horizon? That must be Orion's belt. I raise my binoculars for a better look at the belt then lower it for a more comprehensive, eye-view of the sky. Sure enough that's Orion, the hunter, with Betelgeuse shining brightly on his shoulder and Rigel shining brightly on his left foot. I raise the binoculars again to study the detail of Orion, but my head starts spinning. I have to look away, dropping my eyes to the ground to stave off vertigo. While switching back and forth between the naked eye and binoculars, it's all too easy to experience that.

The December wind rips right through my clothes. I can feel my core body temperature dropping. My hands, unsheathed from gloves in order to manipulate the binoculars, are beginning to freeze up. I can't stay out here much longer so I make one last play for the celestial object I've been thinking about for a while now: Andromeda Galaxy. I thought I spotted it in my backyard a week ago, but the sky was so bleached out by the moon and the town's light pollution that I couldn't get a good look at it. Tonight's a different story.

According to my star chart, Andromeda should be near zenith right now. Zenith is that point directly overhead where the earth's atmosphere is thinnest and the night sky is darkest. I quickly locate the Great Square of Pegasus and hop from one bright star to another towards the constellation Andromeda. Star hopping is harder than it sounds, but eventually I make my way to a critical pair of stars. From there it's supposed to be a short jump to the galaxy.

Is that it? Is that Andromeda? I adjust the focus on my binoculars ever so slowly while holding my position. It looks so . . . otherworldly. It looks like nothing I've ever seen before – a fuzzy patch of light in the darkness. It looks like a large star that's been smeared across a tiny portion of the night sky. I drop my binoculars while still craning my neck, making sure that I'm in the right spot. Then I look through my binoculars again. No doubt about it, that's Andromeda Galaxy. I can barely make out its oval shape. Whoa . . . an entire galaxy of stars, over two million light years away! I can't believe I'm seeing this. I'm seeing the Great Andromeda Galaxy – a spiral galaxy much like our own Milky Way – a sister galaxy in the Local Group.

"Giant galaxies like the Milky Way and Andromeda are vital for life," I remember reading in Croswell's *The Universe at Midnight*. It has something to do with the "heavy elements" found in the many nebulas that populate the spiral arms of such galaxies. That means I'm looking at a stellar system that contains billions of stars much like our Sun, and many worlds similar to our own. And the light now entering my eye left that galaxy over two million years ago. Wow!

The cold is getting to me. I'm shivering now so I'd better call it a night. I lower my binoculars, stepping away from the cosmos. The snow crunches underfoot as I stumble on half-numb legs back to the car. A fierce gust of wind freezes my face. My eyes start watering. After slipping into the car, I immediately fire up the engine in order to get the heater going. As I wait for the car to warm up, all I can think about is how cold it must be out there in deep space. A cosmic chill reaches for my bones, but the car's heater quickly dissipates it, leaving me to ponder the night's observations during the short drive home.

Before reaching my house, I'm overcome by an eerie feeling. I've just seen a ghost. That's how many astronomers describe those faint, deep sky objects. They're more like ghosts in the darkness than the sharp pinpoints of light that we are used to seeing out there. Nebulous, fuzzy, ephemeral – they are nothing like stars, really. Time and again philosophers have asked: "Can we trust our senses?" Right now I'm inclined to say "No." On the way home, I can't believe what I saw tonight. An entire galaxy for chrissakes. How is that even possible?

4

What is real and what is just a figment of my imagination? Rare is the person who can get through life without asking this question at least once, yet most will not dwell upon it. Most people fall back on belief or common sense and leave it at that. Or they use the word "reason" to exorcise the demons of delusion then calmly get on with their lives. But some of us are not so easily consoled. We look deep into the night sky and are shocked by what we find there. We feel ourselves floating up into the starry vault of possibility even while those around us embrace credos that comfortably explain away everything. In other words, we allow ourselves to be philosophers despite the greater tendency of humankind to hold unquestioning worldviews. It's an affliction as old as stargazing itself.

Humankind as a whole underwent a phenomenal cognitive transformation during the 6th Century BC. During that time, monotheism took root in Mesopotamia as Judaism and Zoroastrianism; Buddhism was born in India; and Confucianism and Taoism emerged in China. In other words, we began to construct worldviews that went beyond the capricious actions of *the gods*. Nowhere was this more evident than in ancient Greece. There men were encouraged by a relatively free intellectual climate to think about the nature of the world in a way that went beyond the Homeric myths of gods and heroes. There men engaged in wild philosophical speculation.

Our word "cosmology" is rooted in the Greek word "kosmos," which roughly translates to "world order." The word "cosmetology" has the same root, curiously enough – beauty having everything to do with order and symmetry as the Greeks saw things. But that's another matter. The study of "world order" – cosmology – began with a handful of thinkers in the Greek city-state of Miletus, which is now located in modern day Turkey. Thales advocated a *natural* philosophy in which the world operated according to physical laws. Anaximander invented the idea of the Infinite, turning God-talk on its ear. Xenophanes condemned the anthropomorphism of the day, arguing that there was more to the workings of the world than the mere whimsy of gods. We laugh now, but these were challenging concepts at the time.

Heraclitus came up with the word "Logos" to name the rational principle that dominates all of nature. He also argued that everything is in a constant state of flux. "All things flow," he wrote in one of the few fragments of his writings that have survived through the centuries. By this way of reckoning, the world is constantly *becoming* something else. Not everyone agreed. Parmenides argued the opposite view, that the cosmos was permanent, immutable. Change is but an illusion. *Being* is what the world is all about, Parmenides said, not *becoming*.

The mathematician and philosopher, Pythagoras, came along a bit later with a much more elegant idea. He believed that mathematics ruled the physical universe. He combined science and religion in a way that turned God into mathematical principles that rule the cosmic order. "The music of the spheres," is what he called it, and those who shared his quasi-mystical outlook joined together in a not-so-secret society known as the Pythagorean Order. They were the first to flirt with the possibility that the Sun, not the Earth, was the center of things.

Socrates was undoubtedly the most influential of all the Greek thinkers, even though he left behind no documents. What we know about him comes to us indirectly from his student, Plato. Towards the end of the 5th Century BC, Socrates single-handedly revolutionized philosophy by claiming the existence of an objective truth, quickly adding that it's beyond our ability to comprehend such a thing. When he said this, the Sophists were dominating Greek thought. They believed that truth was relative. The art of rhetoric rose to prominence in Greek culture as a result. In a sense, these were the world's first lawyers, and very successful ones at that. They saw to it that Socrates was tried and convicted by the Greek legal system. He was found guilty of both heresy and treason, and sentenced to death by poison unless he recanted his views. Socrates chose to drink a bitter cup of hemlock rather than change his position. Surely that was something no self-serving Sophist would ever do.

Plato and Aristotle dominated Greek thought afterwards, both men leaving their mark on cosmology. Plato outlined a dualistic cosmos in which a higher reality of ideas or forms dictated the organization of the physical world. This led to God as the Creator. "That which is created," Plato reasoned, "Must of necessity be created by a cause." That was an obvious truth, in a circular way of thinking, so the *Self-moved Mover* came into being – that which creates the world according to its own immutable nature. But Aristotle, a student in Plato's Academy, saw things differently. He saw God as an *Unmoved Mover* who stood apart from creation. Aristotle's God was all-powerful and the world that He made was purposeful, orderly and complete. Is it any wonder, then, that Aristotle embraced an earth-centered worldview?

After dinner on a nearly cloudless evening in mid-December, I venture outdoors to better comprehend the *celestial sphere* and the coordinates that are used to chart it. I already have a vague concept of this system but vagueness, I'm learning, doesn't work very well when it comes to science. I need to get it down pat.

The *celestial sphere* is the name given to that great dome overhead which completely encompasses the earth. The Sun, Moon, planets and all the stars appear to be fixed on this dome, which gradually moves east-to-west. This is how the ancients saw the cosmos, at any rate, and this where our understanding of it begins even today.

The celestial poles are extensions of the Earth's poles. The celestial equator, bisecting that great dome overhead, is an extension of the Earth's equator. Because the Earth's rotation is tilted 23½ degrees relative to the Sun, the ecliptic – that apparent pathway of the Sun, Moon, planets, and the stars of the Zodiac –

weaves through the celestial equator, crossing it twice a year.

Here in the Northern Hemisphere, the celestial sphere pivots on the North Star (Polaris). The whole sky makes a complete journey around the Earth once a day, thanks to the Earth's rotation. The whole sky also makes a complete journey around the Earth once a year, thanks to the planet's orbit around the Sun.

Declination is the latitude of the celestial sphere. The celestial equator is zero degrees, naturally, and the North Star is 90 degrees of arc away from it. And so on. One degree of sky is roughly equal to the width of one's thumb held an arm's length away. Remarkably, my thumb can completely cover either the Sun or the Moon. I thought they were much bigger than that.

Right ascension is the longitude of the celestial sphere, generally speaking. Since we're inside the sphere and looking out, it's a bit more difficult than longitude to comprehend. Where's the meridian or starting point? It's that point in the sky where the Sun crosses the celestial equator on the first day of spring in March. That's right, the Vernal Equinox determines zero. From there the sky is broken into 24 parts, called hours, numbered from right to left, west to east. Each hour corresponds to 15 degrees of arc.

Given an object's coordinates – declination and right ascension – I can find it in the sky any time of the day, on any day of the year. The object in question might be on the other side of the world when I'm looking for it, but at least I know where it is. In theory, anyhow. In reality celestial coordinates give people like me, operating with just a pair of binoculars, only a rough idea where things are. But astronomers wielding powerful telescopes use these coordinates to locate faint objects deep in the night sky with remarkable ease. Back in the old days, high priests would amaze their friends by using this information to predict solar or lunar eclipses. Very big magic, indeed.

Common sense dictates that things are the way they appear to be. That's why the vast majority of people took the celestial sphere at face value for thousands of years. That's why it was so easy to assume from the apparent motions of the Sun, Moon, planets and stars that the Earth is the center of the universe. After all, every celestial object marches across the sky along a common path, in a predictable and orderly manner.

To every reasonable man living in ancient Greece, the universe was clearly *geo*-centric. Aristotle, the granddaddy of symbolic logic, was only stating the obvious when he advocated this view. "As to the earth's position, there is some difference of opinion," he wrote rather magnanimously in his cosmological work, *On the Heavens*. But he was quick to dismiss a *moving* earth as wild speculation: "Most people – all in fact, who regard the whole heaven as finite – say it lies at the center." The key word here is "finite." Although some Greek thinkers had been toying with the concept of infinity for over a hundred years, there was no room for it in the logical, orderly, complete universe that the Aristotelian God had created. And this worldview was widely embraced in 4th Century Greece. After all, it made the most sense.

Indeed, there was "some difference of opinion" among the Greek thinkers of Aristotle's time who were not so inclined towards common sense. Many were members of that somewhat mystical society called the Pythagorean Order. One of these men, Heraclides of Pontus, suggested that the Earth rotates and that's what makes the Sun, Moon and stars appear to move across the night sky. No doubt such an idea made a lot of people laugh back then.

In the 3rd Century BC, the Greek mathematician and astronomer, Aristarchus of Samos, suggested that the Sun, not the Earth, was the center of the universe. He was the first to propose a *helio*-centric worldview – the first we know about, anyhow. None of his surviving writings verify this belief, but another thinker of the time, Archimedes, credits him with it: "Aristarchus of Samos brought out a book consisting of a certain hypothesis . . . that the fixed stars and the sun remain motionless, that the earth revolves about the sun . . ." Unfortunately, there was little hard science back then to support the heliocentric worldview, so the geocentric worldview prevailed.

While standing in my driveway and envisioning the celestial sphere, I empathize with the ancients who caved in to common sense and embraced a geocentric worldview. Things do *appear* that way. But I am too much the modern to share their view. Clearly the Earth moves around the Sun. That's what I've been told, anyhow. But what direct proof do I have of this? Perhaps I'm only a sucker for believing some 21st Century version of common sense. Time will tell.

5

A month ago I realized that I would have to purchase a telescope. Can't pursue my newfound interest in the cosmos very far beyond abstraction without one. So eventually I do what every smart consumer does in a situation like this: I read a magazine article about what to look for when buying a telescope. Then I study a buyer's guide until I am convinced that Orion is the telescope-making company for me. After that, I go online and visit the Orion website. Ordering a catalog is as easy as typing in my address. It appears in my mailbox less than a week later.

The catalog is overwhelming but a few days after diving into it I have a pretty good idea what kind of instrument will best suit my needs. I settle upon a *reflecting* telescope by which the observer views an object indirectly, after it has bounced off a mirror inside the instrument. The alternative is a *refracting* telescope, which allows the observer to look directly through the lens at an object. Refractors are easier to use but tend to be more expensive. Reflectors provide the biggest bang for the buck. That's important since I'm primarily interested in *deep sky* objects and am always short on cash. The deep sky is everything beyond the solar system – nebulas, galaxies and the like. From what I've learned, a 4.5-inch reflector is the bare minimum tool necessary to get out that far. That's why I am seriously considering it.

Magnification is the big trap when it comes to buying telescopes. Go to any discount store and you can find a telescope that magnifies 150 times or more, and it can be yours for just a little over a hundred bucks. But you'll be buying a piece of junk. As with all instruments, precision is everything. A telescope is only as good as the quality of the optics in it. Besides, magnification is only half the story. The other half is light-gathering capability. That's where the focal length of the telescope and the width of the mirror or lens of the telescope come into play. If I'm using a telescope with a 4.5-inch mirror, for example, I can expect a bright, sharp viewing field in my eyepiece at a hundred power (objects magnified 100 times), and a reasonably bright, clear field at two hundred power. Beyond that, one simply needs a bigger mirror or lens to see anything clearly. In that regard the night sky is unforgiving.

Why a 4.5-inch telescope? Because that's all I can afford. A 6-inch telescope would be better, certainly, but it costs more. I'm also thinking that I should start small since I'm just getting into this. I don't know how difficult it's going to be for a novice like me to use such an instrument – how hard it will be to focus, direct at objects, or simply lug around. Baby steps. A 3-inch telescope is considered a beginner's telescope so I'm already jumping to the next level by opting for a 4.5-inch one. Don't want to go too far too fast with this.

Orion sells a 4.5-inch reflector on a tripod for a couple hundred bucks. It rests upon what's called an *equatorial mount.* That means the telescope swivels 360 degrees horizontally atop its tripod, another 360 degrees following declination, and another 360 degrees following right ascension. I get dizzy just thinking about it, but even a neophyte like me can see the advantage of this. Such a device can navigate the entire celestial sphere from any given vantage point.

So that's it. I have found my instrument: a 4.5-inch equatorial reflecting telescope. I tell my wife Judy about my decision and she immediately asks how I'm going to get the money to actually buy this new toy. Good question. The whole rig, including shipping, shouldn't run more than $250, but that's money I don't have to spend on myself this close to the holidays. No matter. Buying a telescope can wait until after Christmas. It can wait until spring, actually. I need more binocular time, anyhow. I need to get to know the night sky better before boosting up the magnification and really disorienting myself. After all, it's a vast wilderness out there.

There the matter rests for a while. With the holidays only a couple weeks away, I soon find myself distracted by shopping, wrapping and decorating. Not much time for stargazing. Judy reminds me that I need to make a short wish list for others to use. I'm hard to shop for they all say. That's when I tell her a subscription to the scientific journal, *Nature*, would be nice. She looks into it only to learn that the subscription rate is well beyond what anyone in our family can afford. Besides, as she puts it rather indelicately: "That journal is for *real* scientists, not mad scientists like you." How very true. So I drop the matter, asking for books, music and hiking socks instead.

With my research into telescopes reaching a financial impasse, I return to more abstract matters. Both the books I read and my surfing on the Internet facilitate this. No doubt about it, we live in The Age of Information. There are more astronomical facts and figures readily available to an inquiring mind than a novice like me can possibly absorb. Almost daily I encounter some factoid that makes my head explode. And there's never any warning.

"The most valued facts arrive unexpectedly, and nakedly unadorned," Chet Raymo wrote in his book, *Honey from Stone*. Unexpected, unadorned and unfathomable. While I'm inclined to dwell upon any given fact for hours on end, trying to make it my own, I'm learning that it's better sometimes to take such things at face value. With that in mind, here are a few of the fun facts that I've stumbled upon lately:

- The Sun is nearly a million miles in diameter. The red giant star, Betelgeuse is over 400 million miles in diameter. The Earth is 93 million miles away from the Sun.

- The Milky Way Galaxy is 100,000 light years across, 1,000 light years thick at the outer edges of its spiral arms, and 10,000 light years thick in the center.

- Orion Nebula contains enough gas to make a million Suns.

- The Sun is 30,000 light years from the galaxy's center and completes its journey around it every 250 million years.

- Supernovas occur in our galaxy once every 30 years. There are 100 billion galaxies in the universe. Assuming that ours is an average galaxy, that means roughly 100 supernovas occur somewhere in the universe every second.

The list goes on. It's endless really. And many of these facts reveal something about the cosmos that is virtually incomprehensible. The human brain can't easily absorb them. It simply doesn't want to go there. But when these facts finally register in our gray matter, a host of implications arise. The most obvious implication is that old cliché: The universe is so big and we are so small. But that's not saying much. We can do better. A more telling implication would be something like this: There's more, *much* more, to the cosmos than meets the eye, and we are only beginning to make sense of it.

On Christmas day, while I'm busy affixing decals to my granddaughter's pink pony castle, my stepson Matt carries a huge box into the room and sets it on the floor next to me. The box is unwrapped so I know what's inside before even opening it. "I thought we agreed not to buy anything for each other this Christmas," I scold my wife Judy, who has clearly reneged on the deal.

"Happy birthday," she says with a great big smile, even though my birthday is months away. "Everyone, the whole family, went in on it," she adds. I open the box and there it is – the object of my desire in a dozen smaller boxes of varying shape and size. I pull out the main tube and inspect it. Then I look at the tripod, the equatorial mount, the counter weight, etc. Then I find the bag of nuts, bolts and screws. This instrument is way more complicated than I thought it would be.

"Technology is a mixed blessing," Chet Raymo writes in one of his books, and that pretty much sums up my frame of mind a few days later as I'm assembling the telescope. My first thought: I'm really more of an arts and humanities kind of guy. After reading the instruction manual twice, from cover to cover, I still don't quite understand how to put the damned thing together. Eventually, though, I work up the courage to try. I do a lot of head scratching. I learn a bunch of new words in the process. I learn words like "azimuth lock knob," "latitude adjustment T-bolt" and "counterweight shaft," – all of which sound vaguely sexual to me. When finally I get the telescope assembled, I stand back and admire my masterpiece. I fiddle with the controls, giddy with anticipation. I think I have just discovered my inner geek.

After dinner, when the sky is dark, I take my rather sophisticated instrument outside. Clouds obscure nearly everything from view but I don't care. The moon is playing peek-a-boo with me. That's good enough for now. I set the telescope squarely in the middle of my driveway and point it towards a patch of open sky in the moon's path. Then I start fumbling with the control cables. Eventually a brilliant white light floods into the telescope's eyepiece. I try to bring the moon into sharper focus but it slips behind the clouds before I can do so. And it doesn't come out to play again. Oh well. On the first clear night, I will be out among the stars. There will be plenty to see, I'm sure.

The folks at Orion sent a disc titled "The Sky" along with the telescope. It's a piece of software designed with amateur astronomers like me in mind. The next day, I slip the disc into my computer and up comes a rather elaborate sky chart that I am able to navigate with the click of a mouse. The buttons on the control panel enable me to zoom in and out of the map, move around in it, highlight deep sky objects – nebulas, star clusters, and galaxies – and learn their names. If I point to an object and click on it, an information box appears on my screen. Sometimes this information is accompanied by jaw-dropping images. That explains why it took so long for this software to load. There are lots and lots of images on the disc. No matter. I'm glad to have them.

I spend the better part of an afternoon surfing "The Sky," clicking on *Messier objects* to see what they look like, and learning all I can about them. Back in the late 18th Century, a French astronomer named Charles Messier catalogued 109 fuzzy objects in the night sky. He designated them M1 through M110, duplicating one by accident. Andromeda Galaxy, for example, is M31. Since Messier's telescope wasn't a particularly large and powerful one, his catalogue is a list of the most commonly known and easily observable deep sky objects. I found out about this catalogue while perusing the astronomy magazine that I purchased last month. But only now am I grasping its usefulness. My 4.5-inch reflector is capable of showing me about two-thirds of Messier's objects. Maybe more, if viewing conditions are just right. This list is obviously the best place to begin a systematic exploration of the cosmos, so I immerse myself in it.

6

New Year's Day, 2004. The sky has opened up so now I can tinker with my new toy. Not long after the sun goes down, I stand in the middle of my driveway, making adjustments to the telescope. First things first: I point it towards the Moon in order to fine tune the "EZ Finder" mounted on top of the telescope's tube. It takes a while but eventually I get the Moon right in the center of the eyepiece. Then I tweak the setting of the finder until the illuminated red dot in the middle of it points to the center of the Moon as well. Just like setting the sights of a rifle.

A quick turn of the focusing knob and the Moon sharpens into view. Wow! I can see the mountains and craters on it quite clearly. The closer to the edge of the Moon I go, the more defined the terrain becomes, thanks to the Moon's curvature. It's easy to imagine walking there. Now I have a heightened appreciation for the instrument in my hands. It has serious optics.

What next? Mars and Venus, of course, located in the southwestern sky. They are shining brightly so they're not difficult to find. The slight orange tint of Mars becomes more pronounced in my eyepiece. No longer a mere pinpoint of light, the planet suddenly has shape and bulk. Venus is colorless but a bit more surprising. It looks like a miniature version of the Moon about three-quarters full. The phases of Venus? Of course. It lies, after all, between Earth and the Sun.

What else can I see? Swinging the telescope to the east, I search for Saturn. According to my sky chart, it is located somewhere in the constellation Gemini. There's a bright object at the foot of that constellation that doesn't belong there. Is that Saturn? I put the red bead of my finder on it then look into the eyepiece. I've got something. A tweak of the focus knob and whoa! That's Saturn all right. The ring is unmistakable.

I pull out the 25 mm eyepiece and replace it with a 10 mm one to boost the magnification. Saturn's ring becomes better defined in the process, giving the planet a distinctly spherical quality. I pull away from the telescope to clear my head. Seeing is believing, it's often said, but sometimes our eyes play tricks on us. I look again, this time trying to wrap my brain around what I'm seeing in the eyepiece. Saturn looks surreal as it hangs there in the middle of nowhere, suspended by . . . what? Space – what a concept. The idea of gravity leaps to mind from my sketchy understanding of physics, but somehow that's not enough to explain what's before me. I want to see the magician's thin wire holding that object in place. I want the trick revealed.

My head reels as I step back from the telescope. Only then do I notice the bitter cold. My hands are freezing up and my feet have already gone numb. How much has the temperature fallen since sunset? It was in the mid-teens then. How long have I been out here? I have no idea. A chill rippling through my body tells me that it's time to call it quits. I pick up the telescope and carry it indoors. The finder and my eyepieces fog up the second they hit the room-temperature air. I leave the telescope standing in the kitchen as I go into the other room to collect my thoughts.

"How was it?" Judy asks.

"Otherworldly," I respond. What else can I say? My head is still reeling. Words fail me.

In his book, *Thinkers of the East*, Indries Shah recounts the teachings of Islamic holy men called Sufi mystics. In one story, a Sufi named Simab was asked to explain his worldview so that an inquiring nobleman could comprehend it. "You cannot understand unless you have experienced," Simab said. And so it goes. All mystical experiences are, by definition, unspeakable. They cannot be relayed from one person to another. You either experience it firsthand or you don't. That's how seeing Saturn strikes me. Another person could look in that eyepiece and see only a little white orb with a ring around it. What's the big deal? It's nothing, really. Just a distant object reflected off a curved mirror. But some of us see more than that. There are different levels of *seeing*, after all. So much depends upon the knowledge one brings to the viewing and what insight one can derive from it afterward.

My first look at Saturn through a telescope hasn't been a mystical experience by any stretch of the imagination, but it certainly has changed how I perceive things. Everyone knows about Saturn. I've been seeing Saturn and its rings since I was a kid. I've seen hundreds of images of that planet in newspapers, books and magazines. I've seen it many times on my computer as well as on television. But seeing it firsthand is another matter. Seeing with ones own eyes turns a mere image into something substantial. Now Saturn is real to me.

Before the advent of the telescope, it wasn't possible to see the rings of Saturn, the phases of Venus, or anything else suggesting that other worlds exist out there. Before optics, our perception of the night sky was entirely dependent upon the naked eye, thus making it easy for people to take the celestial sphere and everything on it at face value. The word "planet" is Greek for wandering star. In ancient times people assumed that the planets orbit the Earth along with all other stars, the Sun, and the Moon, while Earth itself stands still. Aristotle gave this apparent cosmos the *philosophical* footing necessary for educated men to dismiss all other possibilities. And nearly everyone was satisfied. Not until the 16th Century, when Copernicus resurrected that madcap sun-centered theory of Aristarchus, did things begin to change. Throughout the rise and fall of the Roman Empire, the emergence of Islamic civilization, and the general stagnation of medieval Europe, the geocentric worldview held fast.

Claudius Ptolemy, a Greco-Egyptian mathematician and astronomer, took the geocentric worldview and ran with it. He wrote one of the most important astronomy books of all times, *Almagest*, while living in Roman-ruled Alexandria, Egypt – a major center of learning in the 2nd Century AD. The word " almagest" is a Latinized version of the Arabic "al-majisti," which loosely translates to "the great compilation." In that book, Ptolemy described the movements of the Sun, Moon and planets in great detail as they travel across the celestial sphere. To explain it, Ptolemy developed a rather elaborate system of circular motions called *epicycles*, which look like stretched and overlapping springs when displayed on paper. These epicycles were complicated, to be sure, but they accurately predicted the locations of celestial objects over time. And everyone was duly impressed.

How did Earth fit into Ptolemy's great system? It remained the Aristotelian, unmoved point of reference, of course. "The earth can have no motion in the directions mentioned," Ptolemy wrote in *Almagest*, "Nor indeed can it ever move at all from its position at the center." Ptolemy's calculations were so accurate that other astronomers used them for hundreds of years. Seafaring navigators came to rely on them. Consequently, the geocentric worldview went unquestioned.

As the western half of the Roman Empire fragmented into warring barbarian states, Greco-Roman astronomy withered away and the Arabs became the new masters of the night sky. Their interest in it was practical, though. They needed to know the positions of the stars at varying times and places in order to navigate the seas and thus facilitate commerce. A navigational device called the *astrolabe*, invented by the Greeks yet perfected by the Arabs, used the stars to accurately determine locations on Earth. So did the sextant, which the Arabs later invented, thereby taking celestial navigation a step farther.

Building upon Ptolemy's original calculations, Arab astronomers calibrated the positions of stars with greater and greater accuracy. This process began in the 9th Century when the Caliph al-Ma'mun established a learning institution in Baghdad called "The House of Wisdom." There scientific texts from many ancient cultures were translated into Arabic.

Al-Khwarizmi, an Arab mathematician and astronomer, used the stars to determine the position of major landmarks on Earth. These calculations later evolved into the first world map. Al-Farghani promoted Ptolemaic astronomy in his book, *Elements of Astronomy*, which eventually worked its way into the fledgling universities of Europe. Al-Battani improved upon Ptolemy's calculations then published *On Stellar Motion*. In the 10th Century, al-Khujandi built a large observatory near modern day Tehran, where celestial observations were calculated with even greater accuracy, to the tiniest fractions of a degree. And so on. While the remnants of Greco-Roman thought languished on the dusty shelves of Christian monasteries in medieval Europe, the Arabs carried the scientific baton forward.

Both advances in astronomical accuracy and the promotion of Ptolemy's geocentric worldview continued through the latter part of The Middle Ages. It culminated in the 15th Century with contributions made by an unlikely character named Ulugh Beg. Since he was the grandson of the notorious Turko-Mongol conqueror, Tamerlane, Ulugh Beg inherited control of Samarkand – a prosperous city located on a major trading route in Central Asia. Having no interest in politics or military conquest, he focused on turning that city into a cultural center. Science was foremost among his interests so he built a huge observatory. It housed, among other things, a state-of-the-art sextant and one of the largest quadrants in the world.

Working with al-Kashi and a host of other mathematicians and astronomers, Ulugh Beg compiled his *Catalogue of Stars*. It was published in 1437, shortly before Henry the Navigator sent forth his Portuguese seamen to explore the world. That catalog gave the positions of nearly a thousand stars with unprecedented accuracy, surpassing the work of Ptolemy and all those who followed him. One major aspect of astronomy remained the same, though – the presumption of a geocentric worldview. Another hundred years would pass before that would change.

7

Taking up astronomy as a hobby in the middle of the winter is one of the craziest things that I have ever done. I stew in my juices for nearly a week, waiting for the endless grey sky to open up. Every day I'm on my computer, learning more facts and surfing through incredible photos of deep sky objects, waiting, waiting for a chance to see something with my own eyes. At long last, a cold front moves into northern Vermont. A fierce wind breaks up the clouds. The sky clears miraculously. When it's completely dark, I pull out my telescope. The air temperature, which was in the single digits shortly after dusk, is now hovering around zero. I don't care. I dress warm then go outside.

A full moon shines brightly in the frigid night sky, bleaching out many of the stars, but I'm hoping to catch a glimpse of Andromeda Galaxy anyway. Using my binoculars, I can barely see it. I'm hoping my telescope will give me a better view. I point the instrument skyward then take off the end cap. Snow swirling about the driveway shoots down the telescope's tube. I try to ignore it. I use the finder to point my telescope towards the Moon. Then I look into the eyepiece. The tube shakes so much in the fierce wind that the image blurs completely. No matter. My exposed hands have frozen up so I can't use the control cables, anyhow. A sudden gust of wind blows more snow down the tube and that's it – I give up. I grab the telescope with my numb hands and carry it back indoors. My wife, resting comfortably on the couch and watching the evening news, says nothing. She just shakes her head. "Oh well," I say to her, "Better luck next time."

When I was very young, I thought the Sun was a heavenly body much like our own Earth. It just happens to be on fire, that's all. This is, of course, the easiest way for an adult to explain that bright object in the daytime sky to a child. No doubt this is what I was told. It's a better explanation than the myths that our distant ancestors dreamt up, anyhow. But, as is often the case when one looks deep into things, the Sun and all the celestial objects like it are much more amazing than any of the stories told about them.

"It is now known that 99 per cent of the universe is made of only two elements, hydrogen and helium," P. A. Cox states as a matter of fact in his book, *The Elements*. Mostly hydrogen; some helium. Why hydrogen? Because it's the most elemental of all elements – a simple, light gas at the very beginning the Periodic Table. A hydrogen atom has only one proton and one electron. It doesn't get any simpler than that. Why helium? Because it's almost as simple as hydrogen. Four atoms of hydrogen, when fused together, constitute one atom of helium. And how does this fusion occur? That's the amazing part. That's where the real story of the Sun and the stars gets interesting.

The Sun is an enormous nuclear reactor. Driven by the dynamics of its own mass, the Sun generates enough thermal energy to transform hydrogen into helium, over and over. This series of nuclear reactions, called *hydrogen burning*, is what drives a main sequence star like the Sun. The process began about four and a half billion years ago, when the Sun coalesced into existence. Right now, our star is about halfway through this hydrogen burning process. When all the hydrogen has been converted to helium, the Sun will swell into a relatively cool red giant star like Betelgeuse. After that it'll shrink into a red dwarf about the size of Jupiter. Then, for all practical purposes, it will be a dead star. This process is played out time and time again in the universe, accounting for most of those pinpoints of light that we see out there.

Most of the other elements on the Periodic Table are generated inside much larger, heavier stars known as *supergiants*. When the hottest of these stars reach the end of their fusing process, they gravitationally collapse into themselves, sometimes dispersing their material payload into the cosmos by way of violent explosions known as supernovas. Our Sun is a second-generation star, consisting of hydrogen, helium and other, heavier material kicked into space by one of those explosions. The Earth, like the Sun, consists of these same heavy elements, which stem from these same distant sources. Life forms like you and me are made up of these heavy elements, as well. In other words, we are stardust. This reminds me of something Ralph Waldo Emerson once wrote regarding the world we live in: "Nothing in nature is exhausted in its first use." So true. But I doubt that that quaint, 19th Century philosopher ever fully realized just how true this statement is.

The blurry patches of light that we find in a clear night sky can only be one of three things: clusters of stars, distant galaxies, or clouds of interstellar dust and gas called nebulae (or simply "nebula" if we're looking at only one). When we spot a nebula, what we're usually seeing is light reflecting off its gas and particulate matter. These are called *reflection nebulae*. But sometimes we are looking at *emission nebulae*, instead. These are vast seas of gas, with a smattering of heavier elements in them, that are hot enough to emit light all by themselves. Quite often these nebulae are stellar nurseries. That is, they are big enough and powerful enough entities to generate stars.

The Great Orion Nebula is an emission nebula about 1,500 light years away from us. In astronomical terms, that's just around the corner. In fact, this nebula is the closest stellar nursery to us. The odds are good that our Sun originated there, along with everything else in our solar system, including the material that has become you and me. Orion Nebula (M42) happens to be one of the brightest Messier objects in the night sky. No doubt this is partly due to its proximity to us. That means even a novice like me should be able to find it. Orion Nebula is located in the constellation Orion, of course. As luck would have it, that constellation rises out of the east shortly after dusk in the middle of winter. So I'll be looking for it real soon.

No doubt about it, intense passion sometimes borders upon madness. It is now 4:45, ten minutes after dusk, and I'm waiting for the sky to darken. Yet another arctic blast has partially opened the cloudy sky. The air temperature outside, a balmy 20 degrees at midday, is now almost zero and still dropping. But I don't care. I'm going out to look at the stars tonight, as soon as it's dark enough for them to come out and play.

The constellation Orion the Hunter should be arising soon over my neighbor's house directly to the east. Orion stands with his legs apart, one arm stretched overhead and the other holding a bow. In his mid-section is a distinct row of three bright stars known as Orion's belt. And dangling from that belt a sword represented by three more stars. The middle "star" of that sword is the Great Orion Nebula. With this much information, I should be able to find it easily enough.

A large but fast-moving cloud covers the eastern sky during the dinner hour but blows farther east right before the stars come out. I pop outdoors with my binoculars and glass the constellation Orion, which is now clearly in view. I follow the sword hanging from the belt until I spot a smudged patch of light. That's the nebula, I think.

By 6:30 the eastern sky is completely clear. With a western wind still blowing fiercely, I carry my telescope outside. Using the finder, I point it towards the middle of Orion's sword. Then I work the slow-motion controls while staring down into the eyepiece. I'm winging it. There's not enough time to align the telescope to the North Star and use celestial coordinates to locate the nebula. I have to find it quickly before my hands freeze up. It's 5 below zero and the temperature is still dropping. The telescope, shielded by my house from the worst of the wind, still shivers with each arctic gust. Once I have a fuzzy patch of light in sight, I pull out the 25 mm eyepiece and put in the 10 mm one to increase the magnitude. And there it is: a splotch of muted light with three relatively bright stars cutting across it's upper extremity – a bleached-out, colorless version of what I've been seeing on my computer screen for days.

The image is upside down and backwards as they always are in reflecting telescopes, but there's no mistaking what I see. I'm looking at Orion Nebula, a star-making machine 1,500 light years away. In his book, *The Soul of the Night*, Chet Raymo claims that there's enough hydrogen, helium and other material in that nebula to create 10,000 stars like our Sun. I've read elsewhere that it could be as much as a million solar masses.

Ten minutes is as long as I can stand out here with my hands exposed, no matter how much I rub them inside my armpits. But that's long enough to view my first deep sky object through the telescope: Orion Nebula, M42. That's enough for now. I cap the tube of my instrument and haul it back indoors. On a calmer, clearer night, I'll take more time to look around.

As my hands thaw out and the chill leaves me, I try to grasp what I've just seen. No matter how ethereal Orion Nebula may appear to be – mostly dispersed gas that would make an earthbound fog seem practically solid by comparison – it is still a distinct and measurable entity. Orion Nebula is 60 light years in diameter. That's what I call big – big enough to contain our Sun and all the stars in our cosmic neighborhood as far out as Aldebaran. That's way too big for me to comprehend, really.

I imagine stars rolling off Orion's assembly line every few million years, or however long it takes a star to coalesce. That, too, is beyond me. I can *think* of such things but I can't comprehend them. Not really. What does this say about the way the human brain functions? How much further must we travel down the evolutionary road, I wonder, before we can fully understand the nature of things? One doesn't have to look very far into space to be baffled by what's out there. I feel more like a monkey than a god as I scribble in my notebook, trying to describe what I've just seen. Big magic. I'm tempted to sacrifice a goat or lamb in deep reverence to incredible powers of the universe, or at least say a prayer. Even a poem would do. But I end up jotting down rather banal observations, instead.

8

Late evening. I sit in the motel office waiting for something to happen. Sometimes it's like this. During the summer and fall, when tourists are traipsing all over Vermont, I'm often in here doing two or three things at once. But right now, in the middle of winter, there's absolutely nothing going on. So I boot up the office computer and connect to the Internet. I go directly to NASA's Astronomy Picture of the Day website. Haven't been there in a while. Other astronomy websites have been more useful lately – more interesting, anyhow. But APOD is always a dependable source of information.

I have a couple dozen APOD pages to check out, beginning with the Sunday before Christmas. I systematically open them. A few of the pictures are somewhat interesting; others aren't quite so impressive. The one for the last day of the year is called: "A Year of Resolving Cosmology." That gets my attention. I open it and see two green, oval diagrams covered with blue, yellow and orange splotches. What's this?

Beneath the computer-generated picture, there's an explanation that begins with an astonishing statement: "This year, humanity learned that the universe is 13.7 billion years old." My initial reaction is: Bullshit! How can anyone make such a claim? Why would any self-respecting scientist say something like that – something that's bound to be proven wrong in a year or two? I read on. There are a few lines about instruments on a space probe resolving "cosmic microwave background" – whatever that's supposed to be – then another outrageous statement: "The universe is composed predominantly of a strange and mysterious type of dark energy (73 percent)." Finishing the math, they add 23 percent "dark matter" to the mix, leaving only 4 percent of the universe as "familiar atoms." That means only 4 percent of the universe is stuff we can possibly see with our telescopes – material that's apparent to the senses. The rest is god-only-knows-what.

The motel phone rings. I push away from the computer, go answer the phone, then refill my coffee cup. Just when I was beginning to enjoy astronomy, they throw this nonsense at me. Why does it always have to come to this? Damned scientists can't leave things alone. They have to push things to the extreme, making their work unintelligible to the rest of us. They can't resist talking over our heads, going crazy with the facts. Astrophysicists are the worst offenders. One minute they're talking about stars and planets, the next thing you know they are filling chalkboards full of incomprehensible formulas. Why don't they just tell us that 96 percent of the universe is stuff we can't possibly understand? Perhaps I should toss my small telescope in a dumpster right now. Throw my computer in there while I'm at it, along with all the science books taking up space on my bookshelf. Give up now. Sprinkle some magic dust into a campfire, chant a few sacred phrases then be amazed when the fire goes poof! Leave science to the geeks. "Dark energy" for chrissakes. What in the world are they talking about?

Do they think I'm stupid, that I haven't been paying attention? The universe is 13.7 billion years old, they say, but we've been down this road before. For as long as I can remember – for years, for decades, for the better part of my life – the so-called age of the universe has bounced back and forth between 10 and 20 billion years. And all those guesses were based upon the Big Bang theory being a matter of fact. Okay, it just so happens that I'm a true believer when it comes to that theory, but I'm smart enough to know that simply believing something isn't enough to make it a reality.

13.7 billion years old, hah! That kind of mathematical self-confidence is absurd in the face of the great cosmological questions. We're talking big questions here – very big questions – questions dealing with the origin and nature of the universe. The answers to these questions have more to do with the wildest philosophical speculations than anything as concrete as numbers. Modern astrophysicists have gone too far, crossing the line between hard science and pure fantasy. Being a philosopher of sorts, I enjoy speculating about the cosmos as much if not more than the next guy, but I certainly don't try to pass off any of my ideas as facts. 13.7 billion years old for chrissakes. Yeah, right. And Santa's sleigh travels at 98.5% the speed of light.

Perhaps I've missed something. For the longest time, I've been in the habit of reading a book or two about cosmology then forgetting about it for a while. I've been doing this since the 1970s. A lot of science can happen in thirty years. Maybe I should read on. The explanation for "A Year of Resolving Cosmology" is only one paragraph long but it is full of hyperlinks. I click on words and phrases like "dark matter," "strange" and "parameters" to learn more. And slowly, painstakingly, through the course of the evening I begin to understand what these mad scientists are talking about. Continuing my study at the motel the following day, and the following week at home, I gradually put together pieces of their cosmic jigsaw puzzle. And with each cognitive breakthrough I make – despite the fact that my head explodes on a regular basis – I start thinking that maybe, just maybe these guys are onto something. Their facts are quite convincing.

In 2001 NASA launched the Wilkinson Microwave Anisotropy Probe (WMAP), which was designed to measure slight temperature variations in the cosmic microwave background (CMB). These slight variations give us a picture of the universe at a point in time roughly 380,000 years after the Big Bang, shortly after the first hydrogen atoms came into being.

The two greenish oval diagrams shown at the APOD website on December 31, 2003 represent the two hemispheres of the universe. The orange and yellow splotches on those diagrams indicate warmer spots in CMB radiation; the blue splotches show the cooler spots. Curiously enough, this cosmic map bears a striking similarity to the large-scale structure of the universe – the distribution of galaxies throughout space, that is. Not only do the slight variations in CMB lend further credence to the Big Bang theory, but they also provide us with critical information about the nature of the universe. The most important piece of information is the expansion rate of the universe, which in turn tells us something about its composition. And all this from one little probe. Guess we got our moneys-worth out of that one.

Actually, WMAP is only a more sophisticated version of the Cosmic Background Explorer (COBE) launched back in 1989. That probe gave us our first concrete measurement of CMB radiation since a couple guys at Bell Labs stumbled upon it by accident back in the 1960s. But the instruments on WMAP are much more sensitive, giving us a much better picture. And in early 2003, when that picture began to materialize before our eyes, cosmology took a giant leap forward.

What exactly *is* CMB? It's a part of the background noise all around us all the time. That's as close as I can come to grasping it, anyhow. In the February 2004 issue of *Scientific American*, Wayne Hu and Martin White describe it as simply as such things can be described: "Tune a television set between channels and about 1 percent of the static you see on the screen is from the CMB." Yeah, right – now we get the picture. Sort of. Or maybe not. The important fact is this: CMB is remnant radiation that's measurable, and measuring it tells us crucial things about the early universe.

The universe is 13.7 billion years old. Assuming this statement is true, what does it imply about the nature and origin of the universe? If the universe has an actual age, does that necessarily mean it was created? If the universe *began* does that mean it must eventually end? Scientists are quick point out that both time and space were created by the Big Bang so it's absurd to talk about anything existing *before* that event. There's no room for God-talk in scientific matters, it seems. But that assurance doesn't keep guys like me from going there. Like the ancient Greeks, I can't help but scratch my head over the *cause* of it all. Clearly there is more going on in the universe than meets the eye.

"Every natural fact is a symbol of some spiritual fact," Ralph Waldo Emerson once wrote. That's a rather poetic way of saying what we all know these days – that belief and scientific fact are inexorably entwined. One can babble all he or she wants about ancient gods being space aliens, but without facts to back up this claim, who takes it seriously? Like it or not, beliefs live and die by the facts. This is true of all belief systems, whether they are religious, philosophical, or something else. And it always comes down to this: How credible are the sources of those facts?

For thousands of years philosophers have tried to put a finger on reality, differentiating the best they can what is true from what is not true. What makes an alleged fact an indisputable truth? Am I ready to open up this can of worms? Is anyone ever ready? No doubt there exists at least one dissenting voice for every factual claim ever made. Human beings love to argue. They can dispute anything. Even the most fundamental facts about life and death can be disputed. Even the Sun's rising tomorrow morning is not beyond question. Arguments thrive on belief. Reason, it seems, was invented to strengthen some beliefs and dismantle others. Yet when a belief is strong enough, anything

71

goes. It can be illogical to the point of insanity. So why bother injecting facts into an argument at all?

9

January 21st. New moon. Clear and calm this evening – at least for now. It's supposed to cloud over later but I've got an open sky for the next couple hours. That's all I need. The air temperature is in the single digits. That's tolerable. So I take my telescope outdoors for a viewing.

First stop Venus. A strategically placed streetlight makes the planet impossible to see. Damn! Next stop Saturn. Very nice, but I'm not all that interested in planets. Not really. Just biding my time, waiting for the sky to darken. Once it is dark enough, I leave the solar system altogether. I venture deep into the starry realm overhead, beyond the Milky Way, until I find the object of my desire: Andromeda Galaxy. After locating it with my binoculars, I point my telescope at a bright star close to it then use the slow-motion controls to star-hop closer. It isn't easy but eventually I get there. With a twist of the wrist, a big smudge of light fills my eyepiece. I try to bring it into focus. No good. The object remains blurred. It's just an oval patch of dull light with a relatively bright spot in the middle. Not much to look at, really. Yet it leaves me breathless.

"Seeing through a telescope is 50 percent vision and 50 percent imagination," Chet Raymo points out in his book, *The Soul of the Night*. Imagination, yes, that's what separates those with a casual interest in the cosmos from those of us who are absolutely nuts about it. Visually the image in the eyepiece of my telescope isn't all that impressive. It pales by comparison to what one can see on a computer screen – the Great Andromeda Galaxy in all its glory. But there is a big thrill in seeing it firsthand, knowing that the blurred image entering my eyeball has been traveling across nearly empty space at the speed of light for over two million years. It's as much an intellectual experience as a sensual one, perhaps even more so. The mind conceives what the eye cannot.

While staring into the eyepiece, cupping my hand around it to block out city light, I feel the frigid embrace of space. I tweak the slow-motion controls of my telescope, thus keeping Andromeda in view. I keep staring at that blurred patch of light until my mind reaches that other "island universe" out there. Our sister galaxy, Andromeda, also known by astronomy geeks everywhere as M31, invites the wildest speculation. Billions of stars locked in a gravitational dance about a mysterious center. Andromeda forces me to consider all sorts of possibilities. Staring at it is like staring into the eye of God.

When I was a teenager I stared deep into the night sky, looking to the stars for clues about the nature of things. I had "mystical" experiences while doing that, and those flights of imagination came close to driving me mad. Now a real image, albeit a blurry one, enters my head along with the idea of a boundless universe. I step back from the telescope, gazing up towards the night sky, trying to convince myself that there is, in fact, another galaxy out there. Not just one but dozens of them in our Local Group converging upon a common point in space. Not just dozens but thousands, millions, *billions* of "island universes" out there – the vast majority of them moving away faster than thoughts can flash through my head. I am astounded by it.

Regaining composure, I turn the telescope away from Andromeda and wander through the stars of my home galaxy instead. A quick jaunt over to M42, Orion Nebula, anchors me in the familiar. I quickly recognize the stellar configuration near its center as well as the distinct shape of that nebula, marveling at its relative clarity tonight. It's nice to be home. I roam about the rest of the constellation, looking for something interesting until I feel an interstellar chill reaching deep inside me again. How long have I been out here? My fingers are numb.

I can make one last observation before the cold forces me indoors. With that thought in mind, I swivel the telescope westward from Orion Nebula, up and over to the next constellation, Taurus, where there's another deep sky object of interest: Crab Nebula (M1). Unlike the stellar nursery, Orion, the Crab is a *supernova remnant*. In 1054, Chinese astronomers observed a brand new star shining brighter than Venus in the night sky. We now know that they were seeing a very large star exploding at the end of its life. Incredibly violent explosions like this are called supernovas. Crab Nebula is the remaining cloud of dust and gas from that explosion – a dim memory of that cataclysmic event.

Can't wait to see it. I locate the bright star, Aldebaran, and star-hop from there to the where Crab is supposed to be. No good. Can't find it and the cold is really getting to me now. In frigid desperation, I switch back and forth from binoculars to telescope, sweeping the night sky until finally I can't stand it any more. Then I grab my equipment and hobble indoors. Will have to see Crab Nebula some other night.

A blast of warm air greets me when I open the door. I check my fingers for frostbite, relieved to find no grey patches on the tips of them. Then I settle into a soft chair to jot down a few observations in a notebook. I start writing as soon as my fingers are warm enough to manipulate a pen.

Making observations is easy; making sense of them is not. Truth or fiction? Fact or belief? The more I try to lay down a foundation of thought in the firmament of the Real, the more I realize what quicksand it is. In the early 1970s, when I began studying the many religions and philosophies that have been invented since the dawn of civilization, I had hoped to get to the bottom of things. I dreamt of hitting bedrock, of anchoring my worldview in something indisputably solid. No such luck. Since then I have learned how to use logic to argue well, and have absorbed a great many facts, but am not much closer to the truth. The knowledge I possess falls disappointingly shy of the mark. I am not wise. There's a good reason for this. No matter how much I feign objectivity, I remain a *believer* as all people are. And that belief is not suspended when I observe the world around me then postulate about God, the cosmos, or anything else. In other words, my biases keep truth at bay.

Scientists wear objectivity like a badge of honor, but that doesn't diminish the fact that they, too, have their biases. And those biases influence the work they do. The best science is rigorously objective – no one denies that. But objectivity is a tall order – a very tall order, indeed.

Science is further compromised by the Powers That Be, namely politicians, clerics or anyone else who makes rules or controls purse strings. These folks always have agendas to push – *their* worldviews, *their* beliefs, or simply *their* prosperity. Getting around those agendas is extremely difficult, if not impossible. Those agendas have an impact upon the quality of science we get. More to the point, those agendas determine how we see the world around us – what we are told is real. So it isn't easy getting to the bottom of things.

No matter how hard one tries to embrace the truth, there is always at least one group of people doing everything they can to confound inquiring minds. No matter how sincere your quest for truth may be, there will always be an angry mob ready to hang you for it. Socrates was forced to drink hemlock for his rather iconoclastic views. Things haven't improved much since then. The Powers That Be aren't much more tolerant today than they were 2500 years ago.

The Roman Catholic Church had a stranglehold on Western Thought during the late middle ages. To a great extent, the Church determined what was fact and what was fiction at that time. And cosmology did not escape its reach. In the 13th Century, St. Thomas

Aquinas fused church doctrine to the philosophy of Aristotle, which happened to include the geocentric worldview. The neo-Platonists continued arguing the nuances of Catholic theology with Aquinas and his ilk, but no major church thinker or academic at that time dared to challenge the Aristotelian premise that the Earth is the center of the universe. After all, that was a fact firmly established by the great astronomer Ptolemy and reinforced by the best scientific minds of the day. Only a fool would challenge it – only a fool or a heretic.

In the early 1500s, a Polish-born astronomer named Nicholaus Copernicus quietly cultivated an idea that would change the world. Oddly enough, he secured a position as a church canon at Frauenburg, where he upheld Catholic law. He lived comfortably for a while with his uncle, the Bishop of Ermland, at Heilsberg Castle. There he kept a small observatory where he devoted all his free time to astronomical study. In 1514 or thereabouts, he self-published a small book called *Little Commentary,* giving a few handwritten copies to friends. In that book, published anonymously out of prudence, Copernicus laid out the basic tenets of a worldview that sent the Earth racing about the Sun. It was not a new theory. Aristarchus of Samos had said as much nearly 1800 years earlier and other scholars had considered the possibility. But only Copernicus was crazy enough to take the idea of a sun-centered universe to heart, and put his thoughts about the matter down on paper.

Shortly after distributing his little chapbook, Copernicus set to work on his magnum opus, *De Revolutionibus Orbium Coelestium,* which translates roughly to *On the Revolutions of the Heavenly Spheres*. In this book Copernicus outlines the heliocentric or sun-centered worldview almost as an afterthought. As Thomas Kuhn points out in *The Copernican Revolution*, "For Copernicus the motion of the earth was a by-product of the problem of the planets." Ptolemy's rather complex system of epicycles, it seems, did not satisfy the mild-mannered Polish cleric. They did not fully explain the squirrelly motion of the planets in the night sky. So Copernicus found an easier, much more elegant solution to the problem. The planets move around the Sun . . . and so does the Earth!

It would be another thirty years before the cautious Copernicus would allow his book to be published. But in 1543, while he was on his deathbed, *De Revolutionibus* reached print. One would think that such a book would have created a storm of controversy overnight, and that the Church would have moved quickly to suppress it. Nowadays, a controversy of this sort would be an immediate media sensation and people would be snapping up the book left and right just to see what the hubbub is about. But that's not how things worked in the 16th Century. There was no mass media back then and the few scholars who took the time to read Copernicus' book were not much impressed by it.

"The *Book of the Revolutions of the Heavenly Spheres* was and is an all-time worst seller," Arthur Koestler reports in his book, *The Sleepwalkers*. It turns out that Copernican science isn't all that rigorous, either. That Polish astronomer provided very little hard data to back up his theory. His book contains strong reasoning and some good math, perhaps, but little else. More to the point, worldviews do not easily change.

Big questions remain big and our answers to them can remain fixed in place for a long, long time despite the power of reason or any given facts.

"For the earth is not the center of all the revolutions," Copernicus stated quite clearly in his book. Not much room for misinterpretation there. But the Church was willing to live with it. After all, a theory is just a theory. As long as no one used it to question the status quo, then what did it matter? Even Copernicus was hesitant to call this theory a fact. In an introductory letter addressed to Pope Paul III, he admitted that, "It seemed an absurd idea." Truth is, the Ptolemaic worldview was too deeply entrenched in everyone's thinking for the Copernican challenge to be the least bit threatening. Not at first, anyhow.

Great storms sometimes brew slowly. In the late 16th Century, the Danish astronomer, Tycho Brahe, impressed the scientific world with his improved instruments and observational techniques. So when he claimed to see a new star in the constellation Cassiopeia in 1572 and a comet in 1577, people took him seriously. Later he published his thoughts about these curiosities, suggesting the possibility that the heavens were not as immutable as Aristotle would have us believe. Tycho's work cut dangerously close to the ragged edge of heresy. He redeemed himself, though, with a theory of the cosmos that blended the Copernican worldview with the Ptolemaic one. An impossible task? To modern minds perhaps. But Tyco's cosmos made sense to scholars at that time. It went something like this: The planets move around the Sun, but the Sun still moves around the Earth. Granted, the theory is a little awkward, but it was a good compromise between scientific fact and religious belief. And it made everyone happy. Well, almost everyone . . .

Giordano Bruno was a troublemaker. He had a big mouth, too. Born in Italy in 1548, several years after Copernicus died, he had no direct contact with the Polish astronomer. Yet he became one of his most outspoken advocates by the end of the 16th Century.

Raised by Dominicans, Bruno was ordained a priest. But he didn't follow that straight and narrow path for very long. By 1581, he was lecturing in philosophy in Paris. The king there, Henry III, had taken Bruno under his wing. But the French soon grew weary of this cleric's noisy Italian iconoclasm, so he went to England to lecture instead. In England Bruno openly badmouthed Aristotle and his geocentric worldview. That's when the trouble began. Soon he wasn't welcome in Protestant England any more than he was in Catholic France, so he went next to Germany. Bruno continued writing and lecturing into the early 1590s, spreading the Copernican worldview throughout central Europe. But he became something of a vagabond scholar as a consequence, with no place to call his own. Rootless and homesick, he returned to his native land, Italy. Big mistake. Suddenly he was standing before the Italian Inquisition on charges of heresy.

For six years, Bruno languished in a church prison. We don't know whether officials tried to reason with him during that time or use other means to show him the error of his ways. Maybe he was just forgotten. But in the late 1590s, Bruno was interrogated rigorously by church theologians and given ample opportunity to recant. He didn't, of course, so the

Grand Inquisitor condemned him to death for his heresy. He was burned at the stake in 1600.

It's easy to think of Bruno as a martyr for science, but he was really more a philosopher than a scientist. No doubt his blatant pantheism offended church theologians more than his heliocentric views, and his flirtations with magic and the occult didn't help matters. All the same, the lesson was not lost on his peers. Bruno challenged the status quo – the Aristotelian worldview – and was executed for it. Wary astronomers, philosophers and cosmologists took note. They learned to keep their heads down. Clearly any interaction with the Inquisition was hazardous to one's health.

"What is it that transforms an apparently temporary discrepancy into an inescapable conflict?" Thomas Kuhn asks in *The Copernican Revolution*. Good question. It's a question as pertinent today as it was four hundred years ago, when Western Europeans were just beginning to take the heliocentric worldview seriously. As long as people are laughing, or simply not paying attention, all wild-eyed speculations about the nature of the universe are easily shrugged off. And cosmologists remain safe as a consequence. Not taken seriously, but safe. Only when something happens to turn laughter into grimaces does trouble start. Being a philosopher of sorts, I'd like to know the answer to Kuhn's question. After all, making trouble is what guys like me are all about. On the other hand, being burned at the stake doesn't seem like a pleasant way to go. Tough choice.

10

It's Friday night, the end of January, near midnight. After closing the motel office, I stand in the middle of the parking lot with my eyes fixed upon the heavens. I scan the clear night sky, identifying familiar constellations. Then I learn a couple new ones: Canis Major, Canis Minor and Leo. The latter is just now emerging out of the east. What's that bright star in Leo? Is that a planet? I pore over my star chart and, sure enough, it is. That's Jupiter. Too bad I don't have my telescope with me. Whatever. Right now I'm too tired to do anything but go to bed and dream about the cosmos. I'll check it out later.

I spent hours on the computer this evening. It was a particularly slow night in the motel office so I put together more pieces of the incredibly difficult jigsaw puzzle that is the cosmos. Stellar evolution, supernovas, black holes, and dark matter – I crammed my head full of astronomical wonders while longing for a glimpse of the Big Picture. And, yes, that picture is slowly materializing. But I'm still light years away from grasping it all. My head still explodes on a regular basis. It explodes whenever I encounter something that's simply too big to imagine or too strange to make any sense to me. Supernovas are especially big. Some are especially strange – collapsing into black holes. What exactly *is* a black hole, anyway? No one knows for sure. No light escapes from black holes so what can we really know about them? Yet another cosmic mystery.

Reading Chet Raymo's book, *The Soul of the Night,* helps a novice like make sense of the cosmos, but it's like touring a dozen European cities in as many days. My brain can only absorb so much information at once. I run into this problem every time I study astronomy. The scientific details are difficult enough but the Big Picture is absolutely mind blowing. It doesn't help that most cosmic phenomena remain unexplained. At what point will we know enough to venture an intelligent guess as to what it's all about? Nothing less than the nature of Nature itself is at stake here so guys like me are desperate to make sense of it all. But cosmology is the interplay of mechanics and mysticism. No easy answers are forthcoming.

Winter holds the northern hemisphere in its grip. For days it is either too cold or too cloudy to take my telescope outside. Then suddenly I'm making a trip back to Ohio to visit my ailing father. Yet another week slips by.

Wednesday, February 11th. Right now, an hour after dusk, the sky couldn't be any better for viewing even though the weatherman has warned that clouds will roll in later. I go outdoors after dinner to see what I can see. I go to Saturn then Orion Nebula. I discover a double cluster of stars between the constellations Perseus and Cassiopeia. Resorting to binoculars, I find the star cluster M41 in Canis Major but can't locate it with my telescope. I try to find a couple galaxies in Ursa Major but don't succeed at that, either. No matter. The night's main event is Jupiter, still shining brightly in Leo as it was a couple weeks ago. I go to it last. I'm not expecting much so I'm surprised when I see the planet's broad stripes. Yeah, that's Jupiter all right. But what impresses me even more than its stripes are the four faint stars seemingly aligned with the planet. After all, they aren't really stars . . .

In my journal, I'm quick to call those four faint stars the moons of Jupiter, but only after doing a little research into the matter am I certain of it. During the next two or three viewings, I watch those moons move. They trade places over time, all the while remaining aligned, as if a cosmic launderer hung Jupiter and its four biggest moons on a taut clothesline to dry. I lack a true astronomer's finesse. I fumble with my telescope, bumping into it while looking down the eyepiece, and am often disoriented to the point where I don't know which way is up. But even a guy like me can watch those four heavenly objects trading places with Jupiter over time and figure out what's going on. Seeing *is* believing. What a surprise it must have been for Galileo when he first turned a telescope skyward and saw the same thing.

In the spring of 1609, an Italian mathematician and astronomer named Galileo Galilei got word that a Dutchman had invented a "spyglass" that made very distant objects appear much closer. Such an instrument would prove invaluable to generals on the battlefield, no doubt, but Galileo had something else in mind. He immediately set to work making a spyglass of his own. Within a matter of months, he had fashioned a crude telescope that could magnify objects to four times their actual size. By August he had built one that could magnify objects nine times – about what a good pair of binoculars can do today. Before the end of the year, he turned this novel instrument towards the night sky. Then he saw things that no one had ever seen before.

During the winter of 1609-10, Galileo was the first to see the mountains on the Moon and resolve the cloudy Milky Way into thousands upon thousands of stars. After that he turned his telescope on Jupiter and got a real surprise. Like Earth, Jupiter has a moon going around it. Not just one moon but four! Galileo published his observations that spring in a little book called *Starry Messenger*. Later in the year, he discovered that Venus has phases just like our Moon, strongly suggesting that it orbits the Sun, not the Earth. Galileo wasn't one to jump to conclusions, though. He realized that his observations were powerful evidence supporting the Copernican worldview but not indisputable proof of it. All the same he became convinced, as other learned men of the time were, that the Sun was the center of the universe, not the Earth.

Resistance to Galileo's discoveries was stiff, to say the least. When Galileo let scholars and clerics peer into his telescope to see these things for themselves, some saw nothing at all. Others refused to look. Meanwhile the scholars of the Catholic Church, under the guidance of their key theologian and Biblical interpreter, Cardinal Bellarmine, started investigating the matter. Bellarmine asked his in-house Jesuit astronomers if Galileo's discoveries were something that should be taken seriously. The Jesuits said they were. They knew trouble when they saw it. As Chet Raymo recently wrote: "When Galileo put down his telescope, the cosmic egg had been broken, the nested crystalline spheres shattered, and the universe thrown open to infinity."

It took a while but in 1616 Pope Paul V ordered Cardinal Bellarmine and the Sacred Congregation of the Index to take a stand on Copernicanism. They did as they were told and Copernicus' book, *De Revolutionibus*, finally made the Index of church-banned books. And there it would stay until it was "corrected." After all, "petulant minds" had to be restrained. Martin Luther had nailed his 95 Theses to a church door nearly a hundred years earlier. The war between Protestants and Catholics was in full swing. Protestants would use this new cosmology to undermine Church credibility. That was the rationale, anyhow. But the Copernican worldview posed an even greater threat, actually. As Arthur Koestler put it so well in his book, *The Sleepwakers*: "The real danger of removing the earth from the centre of the universe went much deeper; it undermined the whole structure of medieval cosmology."

After the Church's ruling on the matter, Cardinal Bellarmine informed Galileo that he could no longer teach the Copernican theory. Galileo took this censure in stride, certain that time was on his side. Sure enough, a much more enlightened pope, Urban VIII, came along in the 1620s. During the course of several papal audiences, Pope Urban VIII urged Galileo to speak freely about his discoveries. The renegade astronomer did just that, and to his pleasant surprise the new pope showed sincere interest in his findings. That led Galileo to believe there would never be any serious repercussions to his spreading the truth about the cosmos, so he set to work on his book, *Dialogue Concerning the Two Chief World Systems – Ptolemaic and Copernican*. Published in 1632 in Italian, not Latin, this book got a lot of regular people thinking. A breakthrough at last! But to his dismay Galileo was soon standing before the Italian Inquisition.

"May God forgive Galileo," Pope Urban VIII said, "For having intruded into these matters concerning new doctrines and Holy Scripture, where the best is to go along with common opinion." Not until the pope said that did Galileo realize that he was in big trouble. Under the thinly veiled threat of torture – those dark chambers of the Inquisition never far away – Galileo considered his options: stand firm and suffer the consequences or recant? In June 1633, he was tried then found guilty of making "grievous errors" in his book. But Galileo was a good Catholic, willing to admit his mistakes, so the Inquisition went easy on him. His life was spared and a sentence of life imprisonment was eventually relaxed to house arrest. All the same, Galileo was forbidden from writing about such matters again.

Johannes Kepler, a German mathematician who had worked closely with Tycho Brahe, was one of the first scholars to read Galileo's *Starry Messenger* back in 1610 and realize the significance of it. The Italian astronomer's telescopic observations validated what Kepler had already figured out in his head. The year before, Kepler had proved the Sun-centered worldview mathematically, using the data that Tycho had amassed during his lifetime. So he congratulated Galileo for adding a little more empirical evidence to support the theory.

In 1609 Kepler had published a book that outlined his first two laws of planetary motion. Within a decade he would add a third and final law to the set. These laws asserted that the planets moved in *elliptical* orbits around a common point of mass in the Sun-planet system and that the rate at which planets travel along these orbits can be calculated using fairly simple formulas. While these laws might be just a tad too difficult for the average guy on the street to grasp, either then or now, one thing is clear: Kepler was the first person to do the math that fully explains the motions of the planets. And that math still stands to this day.

Funny how things go. The sun-centered cosmos had already been mathematically established *before* Galileo ever pointed his telescope at the stars. In the strictest sense, the Copernican theory was already a fact by the time the Church ruled against it. But fact is one thing; belief is another. Besides, as history proves time and again, there's always a lag between the unveiling of a profound fact and its acceptance. One could argue that this lag is the very essence of history – that without it there would not be much of a story to tell. Big changes take time. Clearly, in 1633, when Galileo was forced to recant his findings, the Copernican Revolution was far from complete. Another half century would pass before Newton would finish off the Ptolemaic worldview once and for all with his groundbreaking work on gravity.

11

In the middle of February, several clear nights of relatively mild temperatures make viewing easy. I take advantage of this sudden turn of events by hauling my telescope into the backyard and looking around. The sky is clearest near zenith so I spend most of my time looking straight up. I drop a piece of plywood on the snow-covered ground and kneel on it while observing. The arrangement is a little awkward, but from this position I can scan the cosmos for well over an hour before the cold gets to me. Half a dozen layers of thermal clothing help. I'm dressed for the arctic. Consequently, temperatures in the teens feel downright balmy.

I begin my observations by orienting my telescope to the North Star – the only fixed point in the night sky. As I slip an eyepiece into the side of the tube and pop off the cover, I am tempted to make a sign of the cross or at least utter some kind of prayer. This impulse might seem a little strange to serious astronomers, but gazing deep into the night sky with a powerful instrument feels an awful lot like a religious experience to me. Science seems like the perfect vehicle for getting at the truth of the natural world, and nature is all we really know for certain about God. This small telescope is my gateway to the universe. If I stare into it long enough, the mind of God just might become apparent to me.

Planets, nebulas, star clusters, and galaxies – a cosmic reality shimmers before my eyes in the cold, dark night. My mundane, daytime perception of things falls away. The sun-bleached sky is but an azure mask behind which God hides. But now, at night, without clouds or daylight to obscure it, the truth is written across the sky in countless points of luminescence that anyone can see. So I genuflect before starting my search.

My first stop is Andromeda Galaxy (M31). After that I go looking in the constellation Triangulum for the other spiral galaxy close to us: M33. Triangulum Galaxy completes the trinity. Along with the Milky Way and Andromeda, it is one of three big spiral galaxies in our Local Group around which the other three dozen lesser galaxies flock. So seeing M33 is important to me. Unfortunately, it is too far west, too far off zenith right now for me to find. I'll have to see Triangulum Galaxy some other day.

I must confess that my interest in galaxies is fueled by a desire to see the hand of God in the universe. Galaxies are great cities of stars, gravitationally bound together, suggesting the possibility of meaning and order. Call it God, natural order, or simply the laws of physics – it's all the same to me. Order is divine and I worship it. Unlike 17th Century churchmen, I see no discrepancy between religious and scientific truths. Semantics aren't that important. The truth is what matters. And I'm sure that there were deep thinkers over three hundred years ago who felt the same way I do today.

The French philosopher and mathematician, René Descartes, was ready to publish his book on celestial mechanics, *The World*, when he heard about Galileo's trial and conviction by the Inquisition in Italy. Then he thought better of it. He postponed indefinitely the publication of that book and went on to write his landmark philosophical works, *Discourse on Method* and *Meditations on First Philosophy* instead. Both of those books reached print within a decade. No doubt René had learned a thing or two about tactical maneuvering during his stint in the Bavarian Army. Sometimes a flank attack is much more effective than a frontal assault. One is less likely to become a casualty that way, anyhow.

"Cogito, ergo sum," Descartes concluded after his exhaustive meditation upon what can be known for certain – "I think, therefore I am." This conclusion may seem laughable to us today, but it had serious implications in the 1640s. For a thousand years, the Church had taught that God alone is the source of all knowledge, and that truth comes to us only by way of divine inspiration, namely, the Holy Scriptures. Yet here was a man – another good Catholic like Galileo, oddly enough – who dared to presume that the human mind itself could not only reason its way to the truth, but could also act as a reference point by which one could orient oneself, just as the North Star orients stargazers to the night sky. Hence, modern philosophy emerged in a form that would later be known as

Rationalism. One small thought for a man, but a major leap in thinking for mankind.

Descartes was no atheist. The verity of his rationalistic claim was deeply rooted in the assumption that God exists and that He is no deceiver. In fact, Descartes' deity has many of the characteristics attributed to Him by the Church. "By the name God, I understand a substance infinite [eternal, immutable] independent, all-knowing, all-powerful," Descartes wrote in *Meditations*," And by which I myself, and every other things that exists ... were created." Indeed, René was a good Catholic, so there was no reason to drag him before the Inquisition. On the other hand, he did get carried away in his reasoning: "I should not, however, have the idea of an infinite substance, seeing I am a finite being, unless it were given me by some substance in reality infinite." From there it was all down hill. After all, it's a short hop in *rational* thinking from an "infinite substance" to an "infinite universe." And while Descartes himself might not have been willing to make that leap, he certainly set things up for others to do so.

About the same time that Descartes was busy philosophizing, James Ussher proved that the world was created only six thousand years ago. Being the Archbishop of the Anglican Church in Ireland, he was as rabidly anti-Catholic as any Protestant could be. But to Christian fundamentalists everywhere, he was a godsend. After calculating the "begats" of the patriarchs listed in the Book of Genesis, Ussher declared the actual date of creation to be October 22, 4004 B.C. This biblical truth was published around 1650 – just in time to head off the word "infinity" at the pass. Lord knows something had to be done. The perfectly conceived and finite cosmos of Aristotle and Ptolemy was falling apart, besieged as it was by the twin evils of science and rationalism. It was just a matter of time before the Sun-centered universe of Copernicus would expand beyond all limits. What then?

Even though Descartes is better known as a philosopher than as a physicist, he ventured a wild theory about what held things together in the universe. He believed that the Sun, stars, and everything else in the cosmos moved along certain trajectories established by some initial motion in the distant past. This "vortex theory" didn't explain things very well, but it did get people thinking about such things. One of those people was Isaac Newton, an English mathematician and physicist, who would took the notion to heart along with Kepler's Three Laws of Planetary Motion and devised a workable theory of gravity.

By the mid-1660s, Newton had his own sketchy versions of the laws of motion, in which centrifugal force played a major role in the movements of planets and other celestial objects. This eventually led to his Inverse-square Law about gravity, which according to my little handbook, *The Essentials of Astronomy*, goes something like this: "The force acting between two bodies is proportional to the product of their masses and inversely proportional to the square of the distance between them." In other words, gravitational attraction is a function of the mass of two bodies and the distance between them. This, of course, later became Newton's Law of Universal Gravitation, which explains much of what's going on in the universe. Gravity may be self-evident to us today, but when Newton published this law in his book, *Philosophiae Naturalis Principia Mathematica*, it was big news. The year was 1687.

Like Descartes, Newton was a religious man. This was true of virtually all rational thinkers in the 17th Century, who's interest in natural science was often driven by a passion to better understand the hand of God in the world. Such men responded to the declarations of Bishop Ussher and those like him with a shrug of the shoulders, confident that science and reason would ultimately prevail, that God's handiwork would be better understood through natural philosophy than biblical interpretation. Despite the Inquisition, this was a time of incredible optimism. And so it should have been.

The unwavering beliefs of Christian fundamentalists notwithstanding, the Western World went from a geocentric universe to a heliocentric one and beyond in less than a hundred years. The 1600s were a watershed in our understanding of the cosmos. As Alexander Koyré stated in his book, *From the Closed World to the Infinite Universe*, "At the end of the century, Newton's victory was complete. The Newtonian God reigned supreme in the infinite void of absolute space ... in accordance with strict mathematical laws." Okay, maybe that's something of an exaggeration, but tremendous progress was made during the 17th Century, no doubt. It was progress in the truest sense of the word, where human understanding as a whole crept forward.

Hard to believe that for two thousand years humankind was locked into a worldview that was (How does one put this delicately?) incorrect. The universe *does not* revolve around the planet we live on, and the celestial sphere *is not* merely a backdrop for earthly events. Thanks to Copernicus and the inquisitive souls who followed him, we have figured out that much. But an answer to one Big Question often leads to more Big Questions. In 1700, we were still light years away from understanding the cosmos at large and some people suspected as much. No doubt Newton himself suspected it. In his famous book, *Principia Mathematica*, he mused: "For it may be that there is no body really at rest to which the places and motions of others may be referred." Hmm... That sounds an awful lot like Einstein's Theory of Relativity.

12

The sophisticated ideas of Renaissance thinkers seriously threatened the fixed, predictable world of our ancestors. The science and philosophy of the Enlightenment virtually destroyed it. Advocates of the status quo had good cause for alarm. Men like Isaac Newton were making sense of the physical universe, and that sense had little or nothing to do with a *religious* interpretation of things. Worse yet, the word "infinity" was creeping into the lexicon of philosophers and scientists alike.

Blaise Pascal, like René Descartes, was one of those French troublemakers who used the word "infinite" in his writings. In fact, he dared to use that word to describe the cosmos itself. "Nature is an infinite sphere," he wrote in *Pensées*, "Whose center is everywhere and circumference nowhere." While this rather nebulous reflection smacks more of mysticism than science or reason, it clearly illustrates the mood of Pascal's day. The boundaries of the universe were well under siege by the 1650s. Towards the end of that century, those boundaries were cracking.

Today those boundaries are practically nonexistent. "Infinity" has become a household world.

Yet contemporary astrophysicists tell us that there are large-scale structures in the universe – galaxies, clusters of galaxies, and superclusters. Apparently we live in a universe that is both infinite *and* orderly. How is that possible?

It's the third week in February. I've been stargazing less than three months and already I've become a fanatic about it. Tormented by unwieldy cosmological questions that the planets cannot answer, I am now reaching deep into the night sky. Reaching beyond nebulas and star clusters, beyond the outer limits of the Milky Way itself, I have become a galaxy hunter. Why? Because structures that big and that far away must surely hold clues about the nature of the universe as a whole; because those working on the cutting edge of astrophysics have told me as much. Those scientists are Sirens beckoning me to the rocks. They draw me towards my intellectual doom.

Recently I've picked up a book that delves deep into galactic structure and evolution. The book is called *Galaxies and the Cosmic Frontier*. Written by William Waller and Paul Hodge then published by Harvard University Press, this book is serious astronomy. Oh boy. I'm in the belly of the beast now. My family and friends know better than to ask me how my stargazing and related studies are going these days. Wouldn't matter if they did. I can't begin to tell them everything that I'm learning. Hell, I can't even absorb it all.

Like snowflakes, no two galaxies are exactly alike, so just looking at pictures of them is a study in the sublime. There are giant elliptical galaxies that have little definition, dwarf irregular galaxies where chaos seems to reign, and spiral galaxies like our own that astound me with their stop-time swirls. There are barred spirals, ringed galaxies, interacting galaxies, colliding galaxies, and galaxies with immense black holes in them. The variations seem endless, and perhaps they are. But one thing remains constant: Galaxies are, by definition, great systems of stars gravitationally bound together. They are "island universes" as some cosmologists have called them. I need to know more about galactic morphology. I must to understand their role in the greater scheme of things. Above all else, I want to see them with my own eyes.

During excursions outdoors in mid/late February, I try to locate several Messier galaxies. I do not succeed. Andromeda (M31) is the only one that I can find. M33 in the constellation Triangulum and those in Ursa Major remain beyond my reach. This is a problem I am determined to resolve. I make a short list of ways to improve my viewing: study detailed star charts carefully beforehand; go out only on a clear, dark nights; avoid light pollution; use binoculars to familiarize myself with the target area; jealously guard my night vision once I've acquired it; make sure the focuser and finder are both finely tuned. What am I forgetting?

Beyond a doubt city lights are the biggest problem. Since I live on the edge of a small town in relatively rural Vermont, I can't complain too much about this. I've seen the night sky from the middle of big cities like Boston and New York and, well, there's not much to see. Most of the stars aren't visible in such places. Even major constellations are washed out by city light. The way I figure it, if you can't see the Milky

Way there's not much point to stargazing. You need that much darkness at the very least.

Galaxies are faint and unforgiving as deep sky objects go. It isn't easy locating them. They push the limits of what a 4.5-inch telescope can do. Fortunately, I have the Internet and my galaxy book to keep me occupied until I get better at using my instrument.

Truth is, the sheer immensity of galactic structures escapes me. But every once in a while, Waller and Hodge declare something in *Galaxies and the Cosmic Frontier* that gives me some idea. "The collision of two galaxies is not likely to involve a single collision of two stars," they state rather flatly in their book. Facts like that make me stop and think about the vast stretches of nearly empty space necessary for that to happen. Here are a few other fun facts about galaxies that Waller and Hodge have thrown my way:

- All galaxies are roughly the same age

- Dwarf-sized proto-galaxies were the first to form

- Dark matter makes up the bulk of galaxy mass

- The number of powerful quasar and radio galaxies increases with distance

- Galaxies tend to exist in groups

I suspect that everything I want to know about the nature of the universe can be derived from this mere handful of facts. But fully investigating such matters would take an entire lifetime if not longer. So I ponder these statements and draw whatever conclusions I can between brief telescopic observations. Mine are only the wildest speculations, of course. I have only a vague notion how the cosmos is organizing itself over mind-numbing periods of time. This will have to do for now. I'll fill in the gaps later.

It was the British astronomer Edmond Halley who encouraged Newton to publish his work on gravity. In fact, Halley corrected the proofs and paid the printing expenses for Newton's landmark work, *Principia Mathematica*. He was one of Kepler's greatest advocates, as well, suggesting that the transits of Mercury and Venus (their passage in front of the Sun that is) should be observed in order to determine the great distances between objects in space. Such measurements would confirm Kepler's Third Law of planetary motion. Halley is also known for discovering the comet that bears his name and predicting its return. That was no mean feat in the end of the 1600s.

Hunting comets was all the rage in the 1700s and the French astronomer Charles Messier got caught up in it. In the middle of the century, he pointed his telescope towards the heavens hoping to see the return of Halley's comet. Unfortunately, the data he used was poor so he missed it. He did discover another comet, though, along with a patch of muted light in the constellation Taurus. That blurry patch would later be known as Crab Nebula – the remnant light from the supernova that Chinese astronomers had observed back in 1054. Eventually Messier would label this nebulous object M1, thus beginning the famous catalog of 109 deep sky objects that we amateur astronomers today all know and love.

The first version of the Messier Catalog (M1 to M45) was published in 1771. During the following decade, the Messier kept adding "nebulas" to his list until he had over a hundred of them. Oddly enough, about a third of these deep sky objects are actually galaxies. Messier didn't know that. One wonders if he would have cared if he had known. After all, some astronomers are more interested in observation than theory.

William Herschel was another 18th Century astronomer big on observation. He, too, put together a catalog of nebulous objects. This German-born scientist settled in England and, with funding from King George III, built several large telescopes – the largest being a reflector forty feet long, holding a 48-inch mirror. Beginning in 1780s, he discovered over 4,000 faint patches of light in the night sky with help from his sister Caroline and his son John. Enlarged and published a century later, this catalog would eventually be known as the New General Catalogue (NGC). To this day, astronomers identify the 7,840 deep sky objects by their NGC numbers.

Just as important as his systematic observation of the night sky, William Herschel speculated about the nature of these nebulae. He identified two different kinds of nebulous objects: those that were mostly gaseous, and those that were clusters or systems of stars. The latter group he called "island nebulae." By the 1790s, he was convinced that these "island nebulae," or "island universes" as they would be called later, were stellar systems similar to but apart from our own stellar system, the Milky Way. In this regard, Herschel was a hundred years ahead of its time.

Oddly enough, it was the German philosopher, Immanuel Kant, who first toyed with the idea of "island universes." In 1755, he anonymously published a book called *Universal Natural History and Theory of the Heavens*, which promoted Newtonian physics. In that book he wrote: "Thus all the suns of the firmament have orbital motions either around a universal center or around many centers." Later he would expound upon this, suggesting that nebulae were "not such enormous stars but systems of many stars." Newton had opened everyone's eyes with his law of gravity, and the universe was growing exponentially as a consequence.

Despite his promotion of Newtonian physics, Kant was no Empiricist like John Locke and the other British scientists who accepted sense experience as the only legitimate basis for understanding. Nor was he a Rationalist like Descartes, who believed that the mind itself is the wellspring of all knowledge. Kant put forth a brand new worldview, a "transcendental" philosophy in his book *Critique of Pure Reason*. Surprisingly, he states in that book: "Space is not an empirical concept which has been derived from eternal experience." What is it then? Well, according to Kant, it is "A necessary representation *a priori*, forming the very foundation of all external intuitions." In other words, it exists prior to our experience of it and can be envisioned as such. Heavy stuff – a bit confusing to be sure – but this much is clear: the worldview of Immanuel Kant is nothing like what came before it. Buried deep beneath all his philosophical blather is a cosmos full of "island universes" that operates on a scale never before imagined. And while Kant himself might have been reluctant to use the word "infinity," thanks to him and the astronomers of his time, the universe was becoming a very big place.

By the end of the 18th Century, many European thinkers were concerned that God's hand in the universe was becoming increasingly more difficult to detect. The more science and reason explained the natural world, the less credible any *religious* explanation of things seemed. How could one bridge the widening chasm between God and natural science? Voltaire and a handful of like-minded French and English philosophers came up with a solution. They called it Deism.

In short, the Deists found immutable laws at work in nature and fashioned that into a religion. Their God created the world then sat back to let creation unfold according to the natural laws He had established. And just like that, the conflict between scientific facts and a belief in God was resolved. Oh sure, a debate still raged between those who saw natural laws as the hand of God and those who embraced a more literal interpretation of the Holy Scriptures, but that would change once the latter group finally came to their senses, wouldn't it? Eventually the fundamentalists would come around, wouldn't they? After all, the natural order of things glorifies God. Scientific facts only make His hand in the world that much more apparent. Surely true believers everywhere – Christian,

Moslem, Hindu, Buddhist, all of them – would warm up to these facts. How could they resist them indefinitely?

13

End of February. A quick look at Orion Nebula through binoculars convinces me that the sky is clear enough to go galaxy hunting tonight, even though a waxing moon bleaches out the southwestern corner of it. No matter. I'm going the opposite direction, northeast into Ursa Major – The Great Bear.

Using my telescope, I find a bright star in the middle of that constellation then star-hop towards my quarry: a pair of galaxies, M81 and M82. I have a detailed star map spread before me on a lawn chair. Right before dusk I printed the map from my computer then studied it carefully, drawing lines and circling distinct configurations of lesser stars to guide me. My flashlight is covered with a red lens to protect my night vision when I read the map. With the air temperature way up in the teens and plenty of thermal layers on my person, I won't be driven indoors by the cold anytime soon. I could stay out here for hours. I've set up my telescope behind the house, thus blocking out light from nearby streetlights. I've done everything I can to facilitate tonight's viewing. All the same, the two galaxies elude me during my initial sweep of the sky.

Anticipating this, I extracted a vital piece of information from my astronomy software before coming out here this evening. I pull an index card from an inside pocket of my winter coat then turn the reddened flashlight on it. On the index card, I've jotted down the celestial coordinates – declination and right ascension – for both galaxies as seen from this latitude on Earth, at this particular time of day, on this particular day of the year.

I learned about celestial coordinates back in December but have been reluctant to use them. It seems like an excessively geeky thing to do: to calibrate the declination and right ascension setting circles on my telescope using these numbers, after orienting my telescope to Polaris within a fraction of a degree. I prefer dead reckoning, star-hopping, bushwhacking through the night sky. That approach better suits my nature. But it hasn't been working for me. Not really. So now I am resorting to math and cold, hard science.

After setting the coordinates in the equatorial mount of my telescope, thus pointing it into Ursa Major, I take a look in my eyepiece. No galaxies there but I do see a triad of stars that I recognize from my star chart. I'm close, very close, so I tweak the slow motion controls ever so slightly. Next thing I know, I'm staring at two fuzzy patches of light, one oval and the other rather oblong. I pull away from the telescope then look again. No doubt about it, that is Bode's Galaxy (M81), and right above it is the Cigar Galaxy (M82). I have found them!

It's no mere coincidence M81 and M82 are so close to each other. They live in the same neighborhood. Together they dominate a cluster of galaxies close to our Local Group. On the cosmic scale, they're just around the corner. And yet the blurred objects in my eyepiece are 11 million light years away. That's 9 million light years more distant than Andromeda. Whoa. I'm getting out there now.

The rest of my viewing is anticlimactic. I revisit Andromeda then a few Messier objects in the home galaxy, but it all pales in comparison to finding that pair of galaxies in Ursa Major. So I pack up my equipment and go back inside to contemplate what I've just seen. I casually tell my wife Judy that I've been to a couple distant galaxies. Somehow the reality of it is lost in translation. I jot down the night's discovery in my star notebook, giving due credit to the celestial coordinates that made it happen, but am unable to say more. I am unable to do anything other than state the mere facts. How strange. The *feeling* of this cosmic encounter goes beyond words, just as most of what I experienced deep in the Alaskan bush did over a decade ago. Wilderness experiences are like that, and lord knows the night sky is the greatest wilderness of them all.

During the course of the 19th Century, the cutting-edge tools of astronomy – telescopes, that is – became bigger and better, enabling scientists to look deeper into the night sky with greater clarity. In the 1880s, the Mount Wilson Observatory was built in Southern California, putting the Americans into the game. Under the guidance of George Ellery Hale, a 60-inch telescope went into action atop Mount Wilson in 1908. A 100-inch telescope followed a decade later. For the first half of the 20th Century, the staff at Mount Wilson Observatory led the way in astronomical observation.

Harlow Shapley joined the staff in 1914. He was given a research position at the observatory, which enabled him to continue the work in celestial measurement that he had been doing at Princeton. Using stars called *Cepheid variables*, whose light varies in intensity over distinct periods of time, he declared the Milky Way to be roughly 300,000 light years across. That made it bigger than anyone else had ever imagined it to be. That also made it big enough to incorporate all the star clusters and other distant nebulae others mistakenly called "island universes." In other words, Shapley's Milky Way *is* the entire universe. Nothing exists beyond it.

Up to the beginning 20th Century, the science of celestial measurement was severely hampered by the lack of tools. As far back as the ancient Greeks, the distances to the Sun and the planets had been calculated by the *parallax method*, which is basically a form of trigonometry. This method uses the Earth's annual position as a fixed point of reference to create a triangle in space whose sides can be determined mathematically. Unfortunately, the more distant the object, the smaller the key angle in that triangle is, making the method rather inexact. That's where Cepheid variable stars come into play.

In 1912, a Harvard astronomer named Henrietta S. Leavitt wrote a paper on the "period-luminosity relation." This paper was based upon the hundreds of Cepheid variables that she had identified in the Large and Small Magellanic Clouds – two "island nebulae" that are relatively close to us. Leavitt drew a correlation between the duration of a variable star's period and its actual brightness, or *absolute* magnitude.

This work was groundbreaking. The *apparent* magnitude of a star is just that – how it appears to us here on Earth. The *absolute* magnitude is the actual brightness of an object. Together these two bits of data can tell us a great deal about a deep sky object. As John Gribbin puts it so succinctly in his book, *The Birth of Time*: "If you know absolute magnitudes and apparent magnitudes for the same objects, you know their distances."

After using the parallax method to calculate the distances to Polaris and a dozen other Cepheid variables that are relatively close to us, astronomers could use Leavitt's period-luminosity relation to determine how far away the various "island nebulae" were. All they had to do was find the Cepheid variables in those deep sky objects, measure their brightness, and observe the length of their periods.

Shapley did not believe that there were "island universes" or anything else beyond our own Milky Way. He argued against it in a famous 1920 debate with another astronomer, Heber Curtis. Like many other astronomers, Shapley based his argument upon the sudden flare-up of a star in Andromeda Nebula back in 1885. That flare-up was an exploding star, the likes of which are better known to us today as supernovas. "To astronomers of 1885, who had not even coined the word *supernova*," Ken Croswell wrote in *The Universe at Midnight*, "so much light coming from a single star seemed impossible." Therefore, Andromeda had to be on the outskirts of the Milky Way. To Shapely and others like him, this was the only rational explanation.

A year after that big debate, Milton Humason approached Shapley with some photographic plates of

Andromeda. On those plates, Humason had marked Cepheid variables with long periods, clearly indicating that Andromeda could lie well beyond the Milky Way. But Humason was the observatory's janitor who had dropped out of school. He had only recently been appointed to the astronomical staff to assist Shapley. Although Shapley was the first to call Humason the best observer on the mountain, he was aware of the janitor's educational limitations. So Shapley wiped the Humason's marks from the plates, explaining why the "island universe" theory was incorrect.

Meanwhile, another astronomer on the Mount Wilson staff was busy making his own observations. His name was Edwin Hubble. He had come to the observatory a couple years earlier with plenty of academic credentials. Unlike Shapley, Hubble had no agenda. As Gribbin wrote, "Edwin Hubble never really subscribed to any theory about the universe at all." He was an observer, first and foremost. So when the facts came in, he took them at face value.

Hubble was measuring the period of a Cepheid variable in Andromeda when reality suddenly struck hard and deep. "On October 23, 1923, he determined the period," Croswell reports in *The Universe at Midnight*, "It was long – 31.4 days – so Andromeda must be distant." Hubble calculated the distance to be one million light years. That's much less than the actual distance we know today – 2.4 million light-years – but far enough into space to put Andromeda well beyond the Milky Way. That meant Andromeda Nebula was its own stellar system. In other words, "island universes" really did exist.

Hubble didn't race to publication. Through the winter of 1923-24, he measured the periods of other Cepheid variables in Triangulum Nebula (M33) as well as Andromeda to confirm his initial observation. He also compared work to the photographic plates that Shapley and Humason had taken years before. When finally the science Hubble had been doing seemed indisputable, he published his discovery.

The New York Times announced the news in 1924 in an article buried on page six. Evidently, the editors of that newspaper didn't find Hubble's discovery any more newsworthy than that. Perhaps it wasn't to the average guy on the street. But scientists and philosophers alike took note. Suddenly the universe was vast – millions of light years across – and populated by galaxies similar to yet apart from our own Milky Way. It had grown exponentially since the days of Copernicus and Galileo. Yet much more was to come. The hard science of cosmology was just getting started.

14

Why is the night sky dark? We can laugh all we want at what seems like a silly question, but the answer isn't a simple one. The deeper into the sky astronomers look, the more stars they find. "If there really are suns throughout all infinite space..." the German astronomer H. W. M. Olbers reasoned in the early 19th Century, "It follows that the entire heavens would have to be as bright as the sun." But it isn't, is it?

Welcome to Olber's Paradox. The answer to this riddle is surprising: We live in an expanding universe. Most of the sources of celestial light – galaxies beyond our Local Group, that is – are moving away from us. Space itself is expanding. But Olbers and his contemporaries didn't know that. So this question boggled the minds of cosmologists for a hundred years, until someone stumbled upon the first hard evidence of cosmic expansion.

Color is the key to understanding the cosmos. An American astronomer with a foreign-sounding name, Vesto Slipher, was an early pioneer in the spectrographic analysis of deep sky objects. A spectrograph is basically the combination of a prism and a camera. Using the 24-inch refracting telescope at Lowell Observatory in Arizona, Slipher targeted spiral-shaped nebulae and ran the light from them through a spectrograph. Then he analyzed their signatures on the color spectrum.

The shift of light on the spectrum is similar to the Doppler effect of sound, where moving objects change pitch as they zoom past us. Distant objects moving towards us shift towards the blue end of the spectrum, while objects moving away from us shift towards the red end. To Slipher's surprise, he discovered that most of the fifteen spiral-shaped nebulae that he observed registered a red shift, meaning that they're moving away from us. He announced this finding in 1914.

A decade after Slipher's puzzling discovery, Edwin Hubble published his landmark work on Cepheid variables, determining that spiral-shaped nebulae were actually whole systems of stars similar to yet independent from our own Milky Way. In other words, there are many galaxies in the universe, not just one. Hubble himself didn't like to use the word "galaxy," but that's what others called his "island nebulas" so the name stuck. At any rate, Hubble quickly realized that the study of galaxies was the new frontier of astronomy. He dived right into it. Taking note of Slipher's work, Hubble broadened his research into extra-galactic distances. Could a correlation be drawn between Slipher's galactic redshifts and the cosmic distances determined by Cepheid variables?

Actually, it was the Dutch physicists and astronomer, Willem de Sitter, who pointed Hubble in the right direction. When Hubble went to Holland in

1928, de Sitter urged him to study the relationship between distance and red shift. Steeped in Einstein's brand new Theory of Relativity, de Sitter suspected that the space itself was expanding. How else could one explain the discrepancies between relativistic physics and the observable universe? Curiously enough, Einstein himself did not believe that the universe was expanding so he invented his famous "cosmological constant" to plug into formulas and hold the universe in place. But later Einstein would call that constant the biggest mistake of his life. Science advances in strange, nonlinear ways.

Hubble compared the data on Cepheid variables collected at Mount Wilson Observatory with Slipher's galactic redshifts. Curiously enough, the two spiral galaxies closest to us, Andromeda and Triangulum, were blue shifted. All other galaxies were red shifted. Then Humason, armed with the powerful, 100-inch telescope at Mount Wilson, collected more data from even fainter galaxies. A pattern developed. The smaller and fainter that galaxies appeared in the eyepiece of the telescope, the *greater* their redshift was. This could mean only one thing: the more distant a galaxy is, the faster it is moving away from us. De Sitter was right – space itself was expanding. Hubble wasted no time announcing these findings. In 1929, Hubble published a short paper on the *velocity-distance relation*, based upon the direct observation and spectrographic analysis of a couple dozen galaxies. Two years later, Hubble and Humason jointly published a longer paper on the subject, based upon twice that number of galaxies. And the idea of an expanding universe was off and running.

As Hubble later stated in his book, *The Realm of the Nebulae*: "The velocity-distance relation is considered as the observational basis for theories of an expanding universe." But a theory is only a theory. There would be considerable resistance to a theory suggesting that the universe is still under construction. There were those in the scientific community – great minds, in fact – who saw the universe as a fixed, immutable, and self-contained phenomenon. After all, that's the only universe that makes any sense.

If galaxies are moving away from both each other and us, and space itself is expanding, then everything must have been very densely packed together at one point in time. How dense? Well, the universe could have been *infinitely* dense. Uh-oh, that word again. Whenever "infinity" pops up, cosmological discussions veer away from hard science, into that ethereal realm where towards where wild-eyed philosophers dwell. Go there and God-talk can't be far away. Hubble and his peers opened up a real can of worms with their discoveries. Soon there would be way too many questions and not nearly enough answers.

After reading a good portion of *Galaxies and the Cosmic Frontier*, I finally accept the fact that 95% of the universe is beyond my ability to observe directly no matter how big my telescope is. The lion's share of any given galaxy is dark matter – gas, dust, planets, burnt-out stars, black holes, stray sub-atomic particles and what have you. As some astute science writer once put it, the light emitted by a galaxy, by its stars and reflective gas, is a lot like the running lights on a passing truck seen at night. It gives you a good sense of what's there, but the greater part of the object remains hidden in darkness. Then there's that mysterious phenomenon out there, dark energy, which baffles even the greatest minds. There's absolutely no way to *visualize* that force. Add to this all the light pollution from cities, atmospheric conditions, and the limitations of my rather small telescope and, well, it's amazing that I can see anything at all.

Only a tiny fraction of what's out there registers in the eyepiece of my telescope. My instrument is no match for the rather grandiose cosmological theories bouncing around in my head, that's for sure. Yet seeing is believing, and I'm still amazed by what I do see.

Back in February, I ordered a *Barlow lens* from the same company that manufactured my telescope. Now it's the second week of March and I'm finally putting it to good use. Astronomy is an expensive hobby. There are all kinds of upgrades and accessories available. I for one don't have a lot of money to spend on such things. All the same, a Barlow lens is a relatively inexpensive way to double the magnifying power. Costing only thirty bucks, I figured it was worth a shot. So here I am, dropping it into my telescope, hoping for the best.

With the Barlow lens in place, I visit a couple familiar deep sky objects. The result is disappointing. Those objects appear larger in the eyepiece, certainly, yet they are much too faint to discern. So what's the point? Telescopic viewing is a matter of light and clarity. I figured that the extra magnification would come at the expense of both but didn't think it would be this severe. The Barlow lens doesn't serve my purposes. Oh well. I'm sure it'll come in handy the next time I look at the Moon, anyhow.

Boosting magnifying power is a common mistake. Every novice astronomer makes it, I'm sure. I've just learned this lesson the hard way. So now it's back to basics – back to clear nights, as much darkness as possible, detailed sky charts, and celestial coordinates. No more quick fixes.

Earlier in the month, I stumbled upon a large, open field way up in the mountains. I was out for the day, snowshoeing around, more interested in getting fresh air and exercise than anything else. But the prospect of viewing the night sky from that field did occur to me at the time. I looked up into the daytime sky overhead and imagined what it must be like on a clear night. Right now, after a rather unsuccessful backyard outing, I'm thinking that I should spend a night in that field as soon as it gets warmer. This coming spring, perhaps. A moonless night when the sky is clear, yeah, that would be the time to be there.

I set aside *Galaxies and the Cosmic Frontier* after reading the last page of it. My mind is on fire. Quasars, galaxy clusters, an expanding universe, the Big Bang – the pieces of the cosmic puzzle are slowly coming together, giving me some idea, however sketchy, of the Big Picture. I don't pretend to understand it all, but I understand enough to say with confidence that the cosmos has some kind of structure to it. There's some kind of order in the universe, that is. Physical laws are hard at work in it, no doubt. This is no great revelation. I have always *believed* as much. But now there is scientific evidence to support that belief. Or is there? Suddenly I feel an overwhelming desire to delve deep into theoretical physics. There's so much about the way things work that I still don't understand.

Whenever I contemplate the fundamental principles of physics – what makes it all tick – Albert Einstein's famous quote comes to mind. "God does not play dice," he responded when asked what he thought of quantum mechanics and the random behavior of sub-atomic particles. I'm no big fan of random events, either. A good picture of a spiral galaxy is proof enough for me that some kind of organizing force is at work in the cosmos. I do not believe for a second that nature is just a figment of the imagination – an abstract concept with no basis in reality. Yet there's no denying that chaos also factors into the Big Picture somehow.

I suspect that the 18th century Deists got it wrong. I seriously doubt that the universe operates like a finely tuned machine. I don't see it as a giant Swiss watch set into motion by the Divine Clockmaker. There is too much violence in grand cosmological events – things like supernovas and black holes. There is too much mysticism at the subatomic level. Yet the universe does appear to have some kind of order to it. Order *and* chaos? How is that possible? What exactly is going on out there? The more we learn, the less we know.

The end of March. I point my telescope towards Ursa Major and find the Whirlpool Galaxy (M51) – the mere suggestion of it, anyhow. The bright moon behind me bleaches out the night sky to some extent. The light from Montreal sixty miles to the northwest doesn't help. But my precise use of celestial coordinates and a detailed star map help me find that galaxy. A twist of the wrist and that cosmic ghost suddenly appears. I'm quite proud of myself. M51 is 37 million light years away – way out there. I've come a long way since my first binocular sighting of Andromeda four months ago. Now I feel like a bona fide galaxy hunter. Ah, if only the sky was darker or my telescope was bigger – what I could see then! But this will do for now.

15

In 1905, a clerk in a Swiss patent office named Albert Einstein published a paper outlining his Theory of Relativity. After studying James Maxwell's work on electromagnetism and light waves, and pondering the results of the Michelson-Morley experiment on the speed of light, Einstein soon realized that the classical mechanics of Newton "was an insufficient foundation for the physical description of all natural phenomena." He proposed that we look at things a bit differently. And the world hasn't been the same since.

Relativity is an easy enough concept to grasp when applied to common objects. Take an observer standing in place, watching both a bird and a train pass by, for example. Obviously the bird and train travel at different speeds relative to the observer as well as to each other. Therein lies the basis of relativity. But combine this concept with the speed of light and, well, things gets very weird very fast. Light reflecting off both the passing bird and train reach the observer at the same time. Einstein reasoned in the face of this that we should be forced "to abandon either the principle of relativity or the simple law of the propagation of light," but there is "no empirical data" urging us to do so.

Therefore, Einstein concluded, our faulty concept of time and space must be abandoned, instead.

In 1916, Einstein published a paper on this General Theory of Relativity, pushing his ideas on the subject to their logical conclusion. If *space-time* is only another dimension of reality, where neither space nor time is absolute, then the straight lines of Euclidean geometry no longer apply to the universe at large. That means space-time itself must be warped. By what? By the gravitational force of massive objects inhabiting it, of course. Here's a concept strange enough to make anyone's head explode. Yet it better describes the world we live in than anything Newton ever told us.

Skeptics were abundant in Einstein's day but many of them were silenced in 1919 when the British astronomer Arthur Stanley Eddington sailed to Principe Island off the coast of West Africa to observe a solar eclipse. During that eclipse, Eddington photographed the light from stars situated behind the Sun. They should have been hidden by it. This proved that light does in fact bend around massive objects. And that, in turn, lent credence to Einstein's concept of space-time. It made other scientist's take seriously the General Theory of Relativity, anyhow. Unfortunately, there were other developments in theoretical physics at the time that just didn't jive with Einstein's rather warped view of the cosmos.

It's April now and spring is in full swing. The air temperature stays in the 40s during the early evenings and there are no bugs out yet. With Ursa Major and other galaxy-laden constellations near zenith, it's an ideal time of year to go galaxy hunting. But the weather is not cooperating with my astronomical ambitions. Lately, even when it's not raining, there have been patchy clouds overhead. And the unthawing earth is kicking a lot of moisture in the air, creating mist. A good run of clear nights comes along but the Moon confounds my attempts to probe the deep sky. So I do what any impassioned novice astronomer would do in such circumstances. I hit the books.

After breezing through a primer on physics and a short history of astronomy, I pick up a used copy of *God and the New Physics*. I take my time with it. Written by a British-born astrophysicist named Paul Davies, it's a good overview of theoretical physics, astronomy, and the Big Questions that have kept all interested parties scratching their heads for decades. As for the God-talk in it, well, Davies delves as deeply into that as he can while remaining ever faithful to the scientific method. "Mathematics is the poetry of logic," he says at one point, thus confirming his bias. All the same, his book gets me thinking about the role that God plays in the cosmos.

Davies makes it clear early on what his book is all about. One chapter heading is: "Did God create the universe?" Another is: "Why is there a universe?" In those chapters, he talks about relativity, quantum mechanics, infinity, physical laws, causation, the mind of God, and more. He touches upon all the touchy issues of modern cosmology, including the Big Bang Theory. Since 1929, when Edwin Hubble confirmed that the universe is expanding, cosmologists have been wondering when, where and how this expansion all began. The moment of creation, if in fact there was one, is sometimes referred to as a *singularity*. The word "singularity" was invented to explain a point of infinite density in space-time that is the core of every black hole. Some theorists think of the Big Bang as a black hole in reverse, kicking out immense energy instead of sucking it in. Hence Davies' statement: "A singularity is the nearest thing that science has found to a supernatural agent."

I want to believe this. I want to embrace a Deistic worldview that makes God the agent who sets off the Big Bang then sits back to watch it all unfold. This seems the most sensible way of explaining our organized yet continuously unfolding universe. But I'm uneasy about the word "supernatural." I can't help but think that's where humankind goes astray, time and time again. Isn't "natural" enough? Isn't nature itself sufficiently divine to inspire awe and deep reverence? Isn't the very existence of order – any kind of natural or physical law whatsoever – reason enough to marvel at the universe?

Causation is the big bugaboo, no doubt. We keep coming back to this, as we have for thousands of years. In science as in all other disciplines, one thing leads to another. Or does it? Perhaps everything is just a random series of events that has only the illusion of order. Perhaps chaos reigns supreme in the universe. The minute we think otherwise, we fall into God-talk. By any name – Logos, Idea, Natural Law, Prime Mover, or Ultimate Being – God-talk is still God-talk. The capitalization of such words is the dead giveaway.

To be honest, I've been humbled in my cosmic quest for meaning. I look deep into the night sky and ask: "What's it all about?" only to learn a bunch of facts and figures about celestial objects. Five months into this quest, I know no more about the mind of God than I did the day I started. I can say what the cosmos *isn't*, but to say what it *is* remains beyond me. And so it goes with all seekers of wisdom, I suppose, whether they use telescopes or not. We philosophers are, by definition, victims of our own lofty aspirations.

"The first principles of the universe are atoms and empty space," the Greek philosopher Democritus declared in the 4th Century BC. Such a simple concept, really, yet it has taken us thousands of years to verify this. That said we now know that all the stuff in the universe can be broken down to the hundred-plus elements shown on the Periodic Table, to atoms of hydrogen, oxygen, carbon, etc. But that's not the end of the story. Far from it. During the past hundred years or so, scientists have been analyzing things at the sub-atomic level. And like the physics of the very large, the physics of the very small has a tendency to get real weird real fast.

It was the German physicist Max Planck who turned the classical physics of Newton on its head, a few years before Einstein wrote his first paper on relativity. Planck started working on the problem of "black body radiation" – the glow of a bar of steel when it's heated, for example – which doesn't make any sense by any conventional way of understanding things. How can a solid object radiate energy? In 1900, Planck published a paper on the subject. Using a little mathematical sleight of hand, he concluded that energy isn't entirely wavelike. It travels in discrete packets that he called *quanta*. The scientific community was horrified by this proposal, of course, for it confused the properties of matter and energy. As Michio Kaku wrote in his book, *Beyond Einstein*: "The idea that light could be chopped into 'quanta' that act like a particle was considered preposterous." But experiments during the next few decades showed that Planck's Quantum Theory was on the mark.

Niels Bohr, Louis de Broglie, Max Born, Paul Dirac – some of the best scientific minds in the world worked on Planck's preposterous theory for decades, fleshing it out. Then the Austrian physicist, Erwin Schrodinger showed that sub-atomic particles have wavelike characteristics, and that waves of energy do in fact consist of particles. The year was 1926. By then Einstein had already publicized his famous formula, $E=Mc^2$, which makes matter and energy interchangeable. So just like that the dualistic world of classical mechanics, where matter and energy are two separate things, went the way of the dinosaur.

In 1927, another German physicist named Werner Heisenberg stated that the both location of a particle and its speed can't be known at precisely the same time, thanks to its wavelike nature. This rather shocking conclusion became known as Heisenberg's Uncertainty Principle. It stands today as a basic tenet of modern physics. Quantum Mechanics, which is the basis for nuclear physics and virtually all electronics, is inconceivable without it. Yet the philosophical implications of this principle rock our world to this day.

"It is difficult to decide where science ends and mysticism begins," Banesh Hoffman wrote in the mid-20th Century, in his book, *The Strange Story of the Quantum*. The minute we propose even the simplest theory about the nature of things, we become guilty of the wildest metaphysical speculation. The Uncertainty Principle suggests randomness, at least at the sub-atomic level, which undercuts the very idea of causation. How can there be natural or physical laws if we cannot be certain that one thing causes another? The quantum world is one of calculated possibilities. Suddenly, it seems, cosmic order has given way to probability.

What does Quantum Mechanics tell us? More than we want to know about the nature of things that's for certain. "It is not space and time that are basic, but the fundamental particles of matter or energy themselves," Hoffman explains in his book. The realities of sub-atomic physics seem to verify this. Yet those who believe in natural order greeted this news with intense skepticism. To the challenge of Quantum Mechanics, Einstein replied: "God does not play dice," and all True Believers everywhere nodded their heads in agreement. But belief can't last forever if the facts aren't there to back it up.

Protons, electrons and neutrons – we learn about basic atomic structure in grade school. We are told that some of these sub-atomic particles race around a nuclear core where other particles exist. The structure is much like planets orbiting the Sun. Is seems very small objects mimic the behavior of very large ones. Or do they? General Relativity and Quantum Mechanics are two entirely different ways of explaining things. The former deals with gravity; the latter deals with everything else. And yet they must be brought together somehow if we are to enjoy a comprehensive understanding of the universe in which we live. If both theories are true, then a Grand Theory must be devised to unify these seemingly divergent concepts. But how do we begin doing that?

16

In the early 1800s, nearly a hundred years before the term "Big Bang" was coined, a popular writer named Edgar Allen Poe envisioned a primordial particle from which everything else sprang. Maybe it was only the narcotics talking, but Poe was strong enough in his convictions to write about that particle in a lengthy prose poem called *Eureka*. He rambles on about it: "Here the Reason flies at once to Imparticularity – to a particle – to one particle – a particle of one kind – of one character – of one nature – of one size – of one form – a particle, therefore, without form and void." But eventually our mad poet says: "The constitution of the Universe from it, the Particle," and there's no mistaking what he was talking about. Before Planck, Einstein or Hubble, Poe toyed with the idea that the universe expanded from a single point in space-time. Or, as we moderns call it: a *singularity*.

Some scientists embraced the idea of an expanding universe immediately after Hubble provided the first solid evidence of it. In fact, the Belgian cosmologist Georges Édouard Lemaître was promoting the idea of an expanding universe in 1927 – two years *before*

Hubble published his landmark paper on distance-velocity relation. Lemaître was an ordained priest, so it should come as no surprise to anyone that his expanding universe smacks of causation. Causation suggests a creation event, and there can't be a creation event without a Creator. Naturally, it was a priest who dreamt all this up. But what takes me by surprise is the fact that Lemaître came to this conclusion by way of relativity.

"The expansion of the universe is a matter of astronomical facts interpreted by the theory of relativity," Lemaître wrote. Many advocates of relativity disagreed, including Einstein. Yet others like Willem de Sitter believed that there was a force at work in the universe that expands space itself. Why? Because *something* has to trump gravity, otherwise there can't be any expansion. Everything is in motion in the universe. Hubble proved that some of that motion is outward, anti-gravitational. But how is that possible?

In 1931, shortly after Einstein went to Mt. Wilson to meet with Hubble and peer through the 100-inch telescope, he took the "cosmological constant" out of his formulas. Originally Einstein had slipped that constant into his formulas to keep everything in balance, to make the universe immutable and unchanging. That was, as he later claimed, the biggest mistake of his life. In due time, Einstein accepted that the universe is expanding. But believing in a moment of creation, well, that's another matter entirely.

The moment-of-creation theory proposed by Lemaître – later known as the Big Bang Theory – was extremely unpopular when it first came out. Most scientists in the early 20th Century didn't even want to talk about it – not even those who had a hand in showing that the universe is expanding. As Dennis Overbye wrote in his book, *Lonely Hearts of the Cosmos*, "Hubble and Einstein both had thought it was nutty. That was the weakest, most incomprehensible aspect of the expanding universe theory. It wasn't science; it was theology."

Who can fault astrophysicists for resisting an incursion into their field by religion? It took hundreds of years for impartial minds to break free from the shackles of ignorance and superstition imposed by the Church during the Dark Ages. It took *thinking* men, brave men standing before the Inquisition, to initiate a long-awaited period of enlightenment where scientists and philosophers could speculate as freely and openly about the cosmos as the ancient Greeks did. Fact-based scientific truths have been hard-won and no quarter should be given to the witch doctors that held science down for so long. A moment of creation? Those are fightin' words!

Arthur Eddington, who traveled all the way to West Africa to make the astronomical observations that proved Einstein's Theory of Relativity, was one of Lemaître's biggest critics. "Philosophically," he wrote, "The notion of a beginning of the present order of nature is repugnant to me." And that pretty much say it all. Repugnance is visceral. Even among scientists, emotions can run high. There is simply too much bad blood between scientists and theologians for them to suddenly walk happily arm-in-arm together down the road to Truth. The trial of Galileo has not been forgotten. Lemaître worked hard trying to keep matters of faith out of his science, but there was no denying the obvious implications of his work.

An English astronomer named Fred Hoyle was one of the Big Bang's most vocal critics. Perhaps it is no mere coincidence that Hoyle was also an atheist. As with so many others, Hoyle's reaction to the theory was largely visceral. He once said: "The big bang idea seemed to me to be unsatisfactory even before detailed examination showed that it leads to serious difficulties." It was Hoyle, in fact, who came up with the term "big bang" to describe Lemaître's moment-of-creation theory. Hoyle used the term disparagingly as he attempted to show the absurdity of such a concept. The term stuck and Lemaître's theory has been called the Big Bang Theory ever since.

To counter the Big Bang Theory, Hoyle devised the "Steady State Theory," which essentially holds the universe in place, making it both immutable and infinite. According to Hoyle, the universe has always existed and always will be. It has no spatial or temporal boundaries whatsoever so there's no need for a creation event. This cosmology had much greater appeal in the scientific community than Lemaître's view and for good reason. In a steady-state universe, the laws of physics are fixed, unchangeable, applying to all things at all times. Reason prevails and science, in due time, will ultimately explain everything. No doubt Aristotle would have embraced this worldview, had he lived in a more modern time. After all, it makes the most sense.

The Russian astrophysicist George Gamow escaped political oppression in his native land, moving to the United States in 1934. By 1940, he was a naturalized American. Gamow brought with him a strong belief in the Big Bang, and that put him right in the middle of the mounting cosmological controversy. In 1948, the same year that Hoyle publicized his Steady State Theory, Gamow and a couple other scientists wrote a paper hypothesizing that an extremely hot, primordial universe created all the elements. As the universe cooled, it expanded with its abundance of hydrogen and helium eventually condensing into stars and galaxies.

According to Gamow and his associates, the stars generated all the other material on the Periodic Table. As P. A. Cox wrote much later in his book, *The Elements*, "Most of the elements present in the universe today come from heavy stars which end their lives with gigantic explosions – supernovae – spewing the products of the nuclear reactions out into space." This is now a foregone conclusion, but in Gamow's time, a half century ago, it was a highly speculative concept too closely associated with Big Bang cosmology for comfort.

Shortly after Gamow's landmark paper, Ralph Alpher and Robert Herman argued that some trace radiation from that hot, primordial universe must remain to this day. This motivated Bob Dicke and Jim Peebles to explore the microwave portion of the spectrum, looking for remnant radiation. At the same time, two young scientists at Bell Labs named Arno Penzias and Robert Wilson stumbled upon a radio anomaly that seemed to be coming from all directions. This anomaly – an ever-present hiss – turned out to be the first tangible evidence of Gamow's primordial universe. The year was 1965. Eventually the radiation causing that ever-present hiss would be known as the Cosmic Microwave Background (CMB).

For all practical purposes, the discovery of CMB killed the Steady State Theory. The Big Bang, while still just a theory, became something that even scientists who rejected the idea of creation had to take seriously. Yet it still reeked of theology. The Roman Catholic Church, so resistant to the Copernican worldview back in the 17th and 18th Centuries, embraced the Big Bang without hesitation. In 1951, before CMB had even been discovered, Pope Pius XII declared the theory compatible with church doctrine. This declaration nauseated many scientists, no doubt. With friends like that, who needs enemies?

At what point does a theory become more than a theory? What causes us to abandon an old way of looking at things and embrace an entirely new one? Overwhelming evidence, of course – that's what any good scientist will tell you. And that's probably true to some extent. The more evidence there is of something, the more people will believe it. But when it comes to matters of fundamental belief – how one views the world at large – things do not change so quickly or easily.

Take the Flat Earth worldview, for instance. One would think that such a belief would have gone extinct by now, considering what we know about the planet upon which we live. But a cursory search on the Internet reveals that a Flat Earth Society exists with something like 3,000 members. The Round Earth Theory, they tell us, is a great lie that was contrived by Copernicus and his co-conspirators to discredit Jesus and the Holy Scriptures. How can anyone argue with that?

For some people, there is never enough evidence. No matter how many facts are presented to support a worldview, there will always be at least one person willing to reject it. No doubt there is someone alive today who honestly believes that all the rest of us are merely figments of his/her imagination. How can we convince that person otherwise? Clearly facts, figures, and logical arguments can only carry a belief system so far. All the same, when enough people take the facts to heart, the course of human history changes. And that change is usually for the best. If there is such a thing as human progress, apart from the silly notion of unlimited economic growth, then the facts are what propel it.

17

At long last, a clear dark night with very little moisture in the air comes along. I've been waiting a couple weeks for this. I lost most of May to bad weather, a trip abroad with my wife, and other distractions. Now it's the 10th of June and I'm finally venturing back into the night sky again. What do professional astronomers do? They live in semi-arid climates for one thing. Perhaps it's no mistake that Mt. Wilson and Palomar – two hot spots for American astronomy – are located in Southern California. The New England sky is not kind to stargazers.

Nine o'clock and it's still not dark outside. The Sun sets late this time of year. The Summer Solstice, after all, is only a couple weeks away. I suck down several cups of coffee while sitting inside, waiting. I study star charts while I wait. It'll be ten o'clock before the Milky Way is visible. No sense looking skyward before that.

An hour after dusk, it's finally dark enough for viewing. I go directly to the constellation Hercules, near zenith, looking for a globular cluster (M13). I find it with little difficulty. It's almost perfectly round. I'm surprised that my 4.5-inch reflector can't resolve the stars in that cluster, even though it has been known as a nebulous object since Messier's time. Perhaps I expect too much of my small instrument. After all, that object is a million or so stars packed closely together on the very fringes of our galaxy. The two irregular galaxies close to us, the Large and Small Magellanic Clouds, aren't too far beyond it.

Globular clusters are an interesting phenomenon. Most of them are located in the hinterlands of a galaxy. If one thinks of a galaxy as a city of stars, then globular clusters are its suburbs. Oddly enough, the globular clusters of a spiral galaxy like our Milky Way inhabit a mostly dark sphere in space that's bisected by a brighter disk harboring the more populated spiral arms. Globular clusters make one stop and think. Why are they so old? What caused stars to coalesce that way? How much more is there to a galaxy than the eye can see?

Next stop, Ursa Major – my favorite hunting ground for galaxies. The tail of the Great Bear is now only a few degrees northwest of zenith. The sky directly overhead is dark enough for me to locate my quarry using a small telescope. With a little searching, I find the very faint Pinwheel Galaxy (M101) – a large spiral galaxy about 24 million light years away. As always, I recoil from my telescope when I first see it. Then I look down the eyepiece to see it again. I'm always surprised to find a deep sky object, no matter how certain I am that it's going to be there. Per usual, the galaxy isn't much see. It's just another fuzzy patch of muted light in the night sky. I stare at it a long while all the same. Eventually, I move below the Great Bear's tail to view the Whirlpool Galaxy (M51) again.

Familiar now with the configuration of lesser stars in that patch of sky, I locate it quickly. This is a much better viewing of M51 than the one I enjoyed back in March. Looking through the Earth's relatively thin atmosphere around zenith helps.

Close to midnight, I wander southwestward into the constellation Virgo. According to my charts, there are a bunch of galaxies there. Near the head of Virgo, in fact, there's a large cluster of galaxies all roughly 60 million light years away. This is the center of the Local Supercluster to which the Milky Way, Andromeda, and the other galaxies of our much smaller Local Group belong. This Supercluster is commonly known as the Virgo Galaxy Cluster. It harbors a dozen and a half Messier objects – galaxies that are visible with a small telescope, that is. But Virgo is too close to the southern horizon, too washed out with light pollution for me to see anything tonight. All the same, I imagine what's out there just beyond the limits of my telescope. And beyond the Virgo Galaxy Cluster looms the universe at large.

Being a morning person, I prefer fall and winter viewing when the sky gets dark early in the evening. Yet summer viewing has its advantages. There's less light pollution late at night, after most people go to bed. More importantly, it's much quieter.

Just past midnight, the cosmos unfolds all around me in exquisite silence. Meteorites shoot soundlessly across the sky. The stars slipping slowly from horizon to horizon are equally as mute. The fireflies that blink in my peripheral vision remind me where I am. They keep me rooted here on Earth. Without them it would be all too easy to lose myself in the stars. The tug of the planet's gravity also keeps me grounded. Without that tug I would surely drift off into the cosmos, towards the Whirlpool Galaxy, the Virgo Galaxy Cluster, or some distant corner of the universe.

There's something profoundly mystifying about the night sky. Despite everything I've learned during the past seven months about the stars and galaxies, I still can't get over the sheer immensity of the universe. I talk about light years as if they were miles, and now find it easy to think in terms of millions, *billions* of years. Yeah, right. As if I could actually grasp any idea of time beyond a few dozen human life spans. Intellectually speaking, I'm beginning to understand the concept of space-time, yet I still use a calendar when I plan for the month ahead, and implicitly trust my car's odometer whenever I travel. The universe may be expanding, but there are still thirteen steps to my mailbox and it still takes six seconds to get there – today the same as yesterday.

It's only natural for us to recoil from the vastness and indeterminacy of the cosmos. There's something about being human that resists it. We want everything to make sense. I'm no exception to this. I gaze deep into the night sky and try to see the pattern there, hoping to translate the mind of God into something I can comprehend. But the universe is simply too vast, too wild. And the harder I try to make sense of it, the more I find myself retreating into those abstract concepts swirling inside my head. This can't be helped. My senses simply aren't powerful enough to absorb the universe at large. Empirical data can only take me so far. Beyond a certain point, all I have are my abstractions.

Of all the abstract notions that scientists ponder, none is quite so heady as the Theory of Everything (TOE), which addresses the most fundamental forces of the physical universe and how they function. In the early 20th Century, it was called the Unified Field Theory – a term coined by Albert Einstein during his unsuccessful attempts over three decades to explain it all. For nearly a century, the Theory of Everything has been the holy grail of theoretical physics. To this day it remains beyond our reach.

As physicists see things, there are four basic forces at work in the universe: electromagnetism, strong and weak nuclear forces, and gravity. In the 1940s, quantum mechanics provided an adequate description of electromagnetism – the force acting upon electrically charged particles. Shortly thereafter, physicists understood the basic relationship between electromagnetism and the weak nuclear force, which is responsible for radiation. During the 1970s, these "electroweak" forces were combined with the strong nuclear force – that which holds subatomic particles together – in the scientific pursuit of a Grand Unified Theory (GUT). This much quantum mechanics could explain. But gravity was another matter. As Dennis Overbye put it so well in *Lonely Hearts of the Cosmos*: "With the advent of GUTs in the late seventies, gravity became the odd man out, the only force not explicable as a quantum game of catch."

Strong and weak nuclear forces, along with electromagnetism, explain how things work at the atomic level. Gravity deals with how things work on the cosmic level. Quantum mechanics addresses the first three. Relativity addresses the latter. But what can explain it all – the very large and the very small? More importantly, what does it matter?

A Theory of Everything matters only to those who want to understand the world that we inhabit. Clearly there can be no intelligent discussion about the nature of our world without some kind of explanation of the forces at work in the universe at large. Nothing escapes a Theory of Everything. Delve deeply enough into Big Bang cosmology these days and you will soon be talking about a Theory of Everything. We can thank Werner Heisenberg and his Uncertainty Principle for that. While rewinding the Big Bang video, we arrive at the frontier of knowing, a mere fraction of a second after the cosmic beginning, where all certainty ends.

The term "Planck time" was coined to explain the infinitesimally small amount of time it takes for a subatomic particle to travel a "Planck length" – for something to make a *quantum leap*, that is. Since the Uncertainty Principle reminds us that we can't know the exact location of a particle and its speed at any given time, we are at loss to explain how the singularity that was the universe in the very beginning made its quantum leap into existence. Or more simply, as Overbye says, "Quantum uncertainty itself determined how close to the putative beginning – the singularity – you could slice time."

So then, how do we solve the ultimate riddle of Big Bang cosmology? Good question. Obviously we need to come up with a Quantum Theory of Gravity before a Theory of Everything can be devised. That is, we need to fuse Quantum Mechanics with Relativity somehow. Impossible you say? Perhaps. But that's where we are today.

Unlike Einstein and his ilk, most scientists prefer facts, empirical evidence, and hard data to intangible, highly speculative thinking. Allan Sandage was no exception to this. In 1949, he went to work as an assistant to Edwin Hubble at the Mount Wilson Observatory. A few years later Hubble died, leaving Sandage to carry on. In 1953, after securing a PhD, Sandage put his hands on the brand new, 200-inch telescope at Palomar. There he slowly compiled *The Hubble Atlas of Galaxies* while continuing Hubble's work on red shifts. Using hard data, Sandage worked tirelessly on the primary cosmological question of the day: At what rate is the universe expanding?

The Hubble Constant (H_0) is a number, based upon red shifts, that determines the rate of the universe's expansion. When plugged into Hubble's formula for velocity/distance relation, it reveals the age of the universe – give or take a few million years. This, in turn, provides scientists with some good clues as to the nature of the universe – most importantly, it's size and geometry. Sandage was all over it. This was a direct, more empirical way of addressing the Big Questions that theoretical physicists had been taking on for decades with formulas scrawled across chalkboards.

By the late 1960s, with the help of the Swiss astronomer Gustav Tammann, Sandage calculated a value of 50 for the Hubble Constant. That put the age of the universe at around 20 billion years. Almost everyone was happy with this. After all, Sandage had the biggest telescope in the world at his disposal so he was considered the authority on the matter. But a young French astronomer named Gérard de Vaucouleurs challenged his findings. He came up with a value of 100 for the Hubble Constant, thus making the universe about 10 billion years old. He argued that the gravitational effects of galaxy clusters had to be taken into consideration, along with other factors, like dying stars that distort astronomical data. So began a dispute that dominated cosmology for the rest of the 20th Century.

No doubt about it, the Big Bang has created more questions than answers. In recent years theoretical physicists have been stopped cold by Planck Time – a mere fraction of a second near the beginning of the universe – while astronomers have argued over Hubble Constant values that are *billions* of years apart. Meanwhile, gravity remains the big bugaboo confounding everyone – the key that will supposedly unlock the remaining mysteries of the universe. It's nice to know that I'm not alone in my grand befuddlement. It's nice to know that I'm in such good company. As far as cosmology goes, these are strange times we live in – strange times, indeed.

18

Atheism, as it is commonly practiced these days, is a belief that there exists no supernatural force whatsoever in the universe. It's a wordview deeply rooted in philosophical materialism. That is, those who call themselves Atheists believe that what you see is what you get, that all things can be reduced to physical components obeying certain mechanical laws. No wonder so many scientists and philosophers lean towards Atheism. The more one delves into natural science, the more apparent those mechanical laws become. And where is God in it all? Nowhere to be seen. Yet there are distinct problems with this worldview that most Atheists, regardless of their intelligence and learning, seem to miss.

To begin with Atheism is, like any other belief system, based upon a set of assumptions. The efficacy of Aristotelian logic is one of those assumptions. Never mind that logic, like mathematics, is a human construct. The universe so closely follows certain mechanical laws that it's only natural for reasoning people to assume that the tools we use to divine those laws are sacrosanct. Surely some immutable Natural Law dominates all things. But therein lies the fundamental paradox of Atheism. Pressed to its logical conclusion, Atheism becomes a religion in its own right, and Natural Law becomes its God. Either that, or an Atheist is forced to declare that chaos reigns supreme in the universe and what we call mechanical laws do not really exist.

On the other hand, there are deeply religious people who embrace the *naturalistic principle*. They believe, as W.T. Stace points out in his book, *Mysticism and Philosophy*, that "all macroscopic existences and events occurring in the space-time world are explicable without exception by natural causes." This means that the laws of nature cannot and will not be broken by the capricious behavior of a supernatural being. This does not mean that mystical events are impossible. On the contrary, they occur all the time. But they occur only because our perception of nature and its reality are two entirely different things. In short, so-called mystical events occur because we do not fully understand the mind of God. If we did, then there would be no surprises, no mysteries, and the universe would no longer seem incredible to us.

All this is heady stuff, no doubt – abstract in ways that most rational thinkers find repulsive. Yet these abstractions are just as essential to any serious discussion about the nature of things as the tools we use to explore the material universe. The arrogance that plagues nearly every belief system, religious or otherwise, arises from the fundamental assumption that *we* have all the answers and *they* don't know what they're talking about. Atheism, under the guise of rationalism, is no exception to this.

Oops, I've done it again. Just when reasoning people might think that I'm actually making sense, I lapse into God-talk. But I don't see how can this be avoided while contemplating the cosmos. The zenith for rationalism was 1929, in those precious days right before Hubble showed us that the universe is actually expanding. Eddington, Hoyle and their peers were correct in their initial assessment of "Big Bang" cosmology. It reeks of religion, and there's no way to get that stink out of it. There are scientists nowadays ready to argue that the sheer indeterminacy of Heisenberg's Uncertainty Principle at the atomic level is reason enough to discard any belief in natural order whatsoever. But at the cosmic level, where gravity keeps things spinning and observers like me remain mystified, absolute chaos is a hard sell. God throws dice when he plays with subatomic particles, no doubt. But at the cosmic level, those dice appear to be loaded.

Clearly chaos does play some role in the world. It is the source of all great mystery – that which neither logic nor mathematics will ever be able to fully explain. While considering this, I think back to what the 14th Century German mystic Meister Eckhart once said: "It is God's nature to be without a nature." As I gaze deeply into the night sky and contemplate the nature of things, I wish I could be an Atheist. I want to live in an immutable world. I'm not comfortable with the kind of indeterminacy that any *supernatural* force implies. But when I ponder the Big Bang and everything that goes with it, all I can do is throw up my hands. The dance of order and chaos in the universe is as mind-boggling as it is inescapable.

The last day of August. After nearly two months of rain and clouds, I finally get an open sky. The Milky Way is visible shortly after dark. Actually, there were a few occasions in late June and early July when I could have gone out, but I was either too busy working or too tired to do so. That's the problem with summertime astronomy. It favors those who can stay up late stargazing and stay in bed when the sun shines brightly in the morning. At any rate, I have an opportunity right now so I'm taking full advantage of it.

The constellation Sagittarius is the main event this time of year. The teapot that appears when I connect-the-dots of the brightest stars in Sagittarius marks the busy center of our home galaxy, the Milky Way. The nebulous, deep sky objects M8 and M22 are easy to find with my telescope. M8 is a large, fuzzy object better known as The Lagoon Nebula. M22 is a globular cluster. There are plenty of other Messier objects in Sagittarius as well, but they're not quite as easy to see. Light pollution is the perennial problem, of course, which becomes more and more of an issue as I drop from zenith towards the horizon. Sagittarius rides low on the southern horizon, just below the ecliptic – that path across the sky that the Sun, Moon and stars of the Zodiac follow.

Around ten o'clock, about half an hour into my viewing, the nearly full Moon emerges from the eastern horizon to wash out the sky – as if city lights didn't make my observations difficult enough. Deep sky objects fade into the cobalt blue background and I'm done for the night. I whip out my binoculars to study the constellations a while before packing up and going inside. I don't learn anything new in the process, but the falling star that suddenly appears is ample reward for my efforts.

While capping my telescope, I resolve to take it high into the mountains for optimal viewing sometime this coming fall, before the snow flies. There's a new moon in the third week of September and another one just past the middle of October. That's two opportunities for a truly dark sky before it's too cold to comfortably spend a night in the woods. If weather permits, I'll be able to take advantage of at least one of them.

19

Monday, September 13th. The sky is partly cloudy when I get out of bed. All the same, the weather forecasters have promised that it will clear by this evening. With that in mind, I take care of some important business first thing in the morning then pack for an overnighter in the woods. I stuff a few essentials into a worn backpack. I break down my telescope, carefully placing it in the padded bag designed for carrying it. By noon, I'm out the door with my gear. By one o'clock, I've parked my truck along the side of a dirt road and am hiking up the Long Trail, south towards Whiteface Mountain.

The air temperature reaches 70 degrees early in the afternoon but I'm sweating as if it was a hot summer's day. I'm overloaded. Along with the 30-pound pack on my back, I have a telescope and all its accouterments strapped across my chest. The uphill hike is hard and slow. I stop frequently to catch my breath. I keep telling myself that the view tonight will be well worth this effort. Besides, the open field isn't far away.

After a mile-long slog, I reach the open field that I scouted last March while snowshoeing. It's about

40 yards wide and a little more than that in length. There's a concrete block hunting camp at one end of it and a small bridge crossing Smith Brook at the other end. The surrounding trees don't extend more than 20 degrees above the horizon in any direction. That means most of the sky will be visible tonight. Right now there are still a few clouds overhead but a steady breeze out of the west should clear them out by dusk. That's what I'm hoping for, anyhow. I hide my telescope in the woods, fifty yards from the clearing, then continue up the trail to a favorite camping spot half a mile away.

Mid-afternoon, I set up camp. I've been in this spot many times before. There's easy access to the brook here and the site is far enough from the trail to remain unseen by any passing hikers. My camp is a humble one: small fire circle with a pile of wood next to it, a tarp stretched over a flat spot on the forest floor, and my pack strapped to the trunk of a middle-aged birch. A bright orange food bag dangles from a nearby hemlock. I'm home for the night. All I have to do now is wait for dusk.

I take a short nap in anticipation of the long evening ahead. After that, I build a fire and boil up water for coffee. Dinner is a minor affair: some trail mix, a granola bar and some crackers. That will do. I didn't come out here to feast. Once I've downed the coffee, I snuff out the fire and hike back to the open field. It's late enough in the day to set up.

Retrieving the telescope from the woods feels a bit strange. The urban part of my mind half expects it to be missing, or at least damaged. But there it is, right where I left it, completely untouched. Evidently the local chipmunks and squirrels aren't the least bit interested in stargazing.

Upon reaching the open field, I spread a plastic sheet across the ground. This will minimize the possibility of losing a wing nut or something to the grass when I break down my telescope after tonight's viewing. After all, it'll be dark then – real dark – and all I have for illumination is a pocket flashlight. The logistics of this outing have been somewhat complex. I usually keep things simple when I go into the woods, but a telescope is a fussy instrument with lots of detachable parts. The more I thought about it, the more I realized that this plastic sheet would be an essential piece of equipment.

I set up the tripod in the middle of the plastic sheet after attaching the equatorial mount to it. Then I attach the counterweight and tube. The slow motion cables go on last. Once the telescope is assembled, I balance the tube and point it northward. Precise orientation to Polaris can't happen until it's dark enough to see that star, but I do everything short of that, including adjustment of the finder and focusing the eyepiece. A half hour shy of dusk, the instrument is ready to go. Now all I have to do is wait.

As the last few wispy clouds clear out of the sky, I light up a cigar to celebrate my good fortune. At long last, I have obtained optimal conditions for viewing. I'm in the mountains, around 1500 feet, far from city lights. There's no moon tonight and the sky is clearing. This could be the best night of stargazing all year. I'm excited by the prospect and more than just a little curious about what I might see tonight. But the

Sun is taking its sweet time settling into the western horizon. Patience, patience.

The air chills out immediately after the Sun slips beneath the trees. Suddenly I realize that I'm not dressed warm enough so I hike back to camp to put on another layer of clothing. The round trip takes a little over a half hour. By the time I get back to my telescope, the sky is cobalt blue. Vega, the first star of the evening, shines directly overhead. I think that's Mars to the west and Saturn to the south, but I'm not sure. I'll be another half hour before the brightest stars of the constellations come out to orient me.

The crimson and gold hues of the surrounding trees have faded to black, as have the white asters, blue gentian and other late summer flowers nearby. A bat circles overhead for a short while. An owl hoots in the distance. Crickets chirp incessantly as the brook gurgles. Other than that, an eerie silence prevails. Never before has the unfolding of the night sky seemed so dramatic – more like the slow removal of a veil than anything else. An hour ago, this was a commonplace world. Now I am on a planet in the cosmos. The gradual revelation of the heavens overhead drives this point home.

"The eternal silence of these infinite spaces fills me with dread," Blaise Pascal once said. As the stars emerge, giving the sky overhead immeasurable depth and breadth, I understand this sentiment but don't share it. I revel in the great mystery unfolding before me, delighting in the sheer immensity of space with its countless points of light, mind-boggling distances, and seemingly endless darkness. Its deep silence is proof enough that the senses are not enough for this adventure. The mind also plays a role in any journey into the cosmos. I am ready and eager to embark.

The temperature has dropped ten degrees since sundown, causing moisture to condense on the telescope's tube. I wipe some of it away before removing the cap. I orient my telescope to Polaris then do a little scouting with my binoculars. This advance binocular work is the only way to get a good sense of the night sky. It's a very busy place tonight, absolutely teeming with stars. But in due time I know my way around. I click on the red dot inside the telescope's finder, focus it, and away I go.

Being a nature lover, I suppose it was only a matter of time before I ventured into the stars. But the cosmos is no place for a down-to-earth naturalist. "Indeed, there is a greater nature up here, a nature that does not abhor a vacuum or trust a parallel line," Guy Murchie wrote in *Music of the Spheres*. "Space is where heat no longer rises ... where gravity can push as well as pull ... where you must be on constant guard against the dangers of 'common sense'." Yes indeed, the *dangers* of common sense. Deep in the cosmos, it will lead you astray.

I am attracted to the order that's so readily found in the natural world. Chaos can be ignored when you're studying an ecosystem like the forest where everything plays a role, where everything has its place. But the incredible explosions of supernovas, the mysterious nature of black holes, the power of quasars, and the sheer magnitude of galactic superclusters are as stupefying as the evolution of the universe as a whole. Euclidian geometry is a given assumption in any patch of wild country here on the planet, but it's virtually meaningless in deep space. Beware, stellar traveler, beware! The night sky is not the coddling Mother Nature that we all know and love. Off planet, the word "nature" takes on an entirely different meaning.

Sagittarius is so clear right now that finding the center of our galaxy is no harder than pointing my telescope at the constellation's teapot configuration of stars. I use the spout of that teapot as a jumping off point and am soon in the thick of nebulous phenomena. Which is which? The Lagoon Nebula (M8) is easy enough to identify simply because I've been there before. Another diffuse nebula, M20, is right next to it. Don't know how I missed it during my August viewing. Both nebulas are large, cloudy objects with luminescent centers. Unmistakable.

Wandering farther up the Milky Way, towards zenith, I stumble upon several other nebulas and numerous star clusters. This part of the night sky is busy, indeed. I could spend the entire night just trying to identify the many deep sky objects here. But I keep wandering instead, following the main stream of stars. Is that M17, the Horseshoe Nebula? I think so, but I don't want to waste time checking my star charts to verify that. I keep going, through the constellations Scutum and Aquila, until I come to where the planetary nebula M27 should be. Don't find it right away so I keep going, right through Cygnus. I sail through a sea of stars, driven forward by mad curiosity. What's next? This portion of sky is quite familiar but never have I seen so much here. Never has it been so receptive to my probing eyes.

After traveling the Milky Way as far as the constellation Cepheus, I stray into Draco and Hercules, sweeping around the darkest part of the sky near zenith. I stumble into a couple more nebulous objects – one of them being the globular cluster M13, I think. Then I step back from my telescope to see the entire Milky Way with naked eyes. Amazing. Is that Andromeda Galaxy to the northeast? It's in the right place. I point my telescope that direction and, sure enough, that huge spiral fills my eyepiece. The center of that distant object is fuzzy yet its outline is clearly defined against a black background.

I swivel my telescope to the northwest, going into Ursa Major next, looking around for more galaxies. I navigate by lighthouse stars only, dead reckoning between them. There's no time for celestial coordinates. Then vertigo strikes. I step away from the telescope, rubbing my strained eyes. Opening them, I focus on the nearby silhouette of a conifer to keep my head from spinning.

Turning back towards Sagittarius again, I wander back down through the Milky Way. Then a simple fact strikes hard and fast: Every star that I see belongs to the home galaxy. Beyond these visible stars, there are only other galaxies. Stepping away from the telescope then turning slowly in a full circle, I actually see it – not this or that constellation, but a swarm of stars buzzing around a galactic center. And here I am on a planet right in the thick of it. I'm surrounded by a vast wilderness of stars.

I've hit a wall. The coffee I drank this afternoon has lost its effect. I could continue observing but I think I've seen enough. Stars are swirling in my head now and the insidious chill of deep space has worked its way into my bones. Time to call it quits. I switch off the red light in my focuser and cap the tube. Breaking down the telescope in the pitch dark takes a while. I do it mostly by touch and memory. The weak beam of my flashlight is more of a hindrance than an aid until I scan the plastic ground cloth for any stray parts. Half an hour after capping the tube, I have the instrument all packed up and ready to travel. Then I haul it back to camp.

The cosmos follows me down the trail – stars shining brightly overhead through intermittent breaks in the forest canopy. My flashlight clearly illuminates the path underfoot yet darkness clings to my shoulders all the same. Even when I leave the trail, groping through the dense brush back towards camp, the brightest points of light still penetrate the tangle of branches and leaves above. The cosmos refuses to let go of me. Even when I'm back in camp, there are enough stars visible through the trees to make it clear that I am on a planet spinning through the cosmos. And I can't shake off that deep space chill.

20

Morning comes with the screech of a blue jay. I awaken to diffuse daylight illuminating the tree trunks around my camp and a few distinct sunbeams penetrating the canopy overhead. The forest looks chaotic – almost as wild, dangerous, and forbidding as the deep, dark sky that I wandered through last night. The ghostly-white Indian pipe flowers on the forest floor look like they belong in a science fiction movie, as do the twisted and multi-colored mushrooms nearby. An inchworm works its way down from a tree branch on an invisible thread. A spider crawls out of my telescope bag. The cricket that is directly in my line of vision and less than a foot away looks especially alien. The manic laughter of a pileated woodpecker startles me. Are these the same life forms I have known all my life? Is this my home planet, or have I been transported elsewhere during my sleep?

It was a cold night last night with temperatures steadily dropping until daybreak. I saw my breath when I got up to pee a few hours ago. The chill of deep space that I felt while stargazing never left me. Even now I feel it deep in my bones. I crawl from my sleeping bag, going down to the brook to splash a little frigid water on my face. Then I start a fire. Just another day in the woods, I keep telling myself. I've done this many times before. There's nothing unusual about being out here.

I awoke several times during the course of the night only to see stars shining through the forest canopy overhead – a constant reminder that I'm on a planet spinning through space. Thoughts and dreams blurred as I drifted in and out of consciousness. The cosmos crept into my head, sweeping away the last comfortable illusions about the world that I inhabit. Earth is just another planet – a water planet teeming with life therefore somewhat unusual, but surely not the only one of its kind in a universe so vast. Everything is transmogrifying – rocks, streams, forests, oceans, and all living creatures. Even planets come and go. Big stars collapse into themselves – some of them supernova into oblivion. Little stars simply burn out. Galaxies merge into each other. The entire universe is constantly reinventing itself, organizing ... or is it giving in to chaos? Either way, it is always changing, dynamic.

"Chaos is an inevitable consequence of complexity," Chet Raymo once wrote. "Law and chaos are the dual creative principles of nature," he then added, driving his point home. These principles I understand viscerally. The tension between them is exactly what I'm feeling right now. A remnant of last night's cosmic vertigo has stayed with me. It feels much like the nausea I experience whenever I contemplate the contradictions of my own existence. "So what is it, then – law or chaos?" I shout into the universe. "Yes!" the stars respond, turning my query into a joke. And my head keeps on spinning.

I see the contradictions of law and chaos in the most elemental things around me. The great mystery of the universe isn't limited to those vast, nebulous objects deep in the night sky. Here on my home turf, in the rocks and trees and streams that I've known my whole life, it thrives. Heraclitus was right. Everything is in flux. Everything is up for grabs, forever changing, even the nature of nature itself.

I build a fire to shake off the cosmic chill. The fire warms my body but not my soul. The flames dancing before me demonstrate the ethereal nature of the most tangible aspects of the world. What is fire but matter transforming into heat and light? I eat a bowl of cereal, thus fueling my inner fire, then boil up water for coffee. I glance at the bagged telescope resting beneath the tarp and feel the full extent of my own absurdity: backwoods philosopher armed with a star-traveling instrument. I roam the planet and gaze upon the stars. I question things, I ponder. More rational, earthbound thinkers stick to the facts. They leave wild speculation out of their equations. I should be more like them. But no, I am compelled to contemplate the unknowable. So here I am with a host of contradictions churning in my gut, feeling utterly absurd.

Just now the Sun pokes above the ridge behind me. It shines brightly over my shoulder. The life-giving home star renders its opinion on the nature of things, saying with beams of light what cannot be said with words. Like most of the visible universe, the Sun is hydrogen burning at temperatures way off the human scale. It's so bright that even here, 90 million miles away, I can't look directly at it for very long. Such power, such intensity! Give credit where credit is due: the Sun knows the mind of God in a way that I never will. It harbors a nuclear wisdom. The synapses that spark in my brain pale by comparison.

Time to go. I've wandered through the cosmos long enough. It's time to go home and take care of mundane affairs. It's time to try to make sense of all that I encountered last night. So I pack up my things and hike out. But the Sun, like the stars that followed me back to camp last the night, hounds me all the way. Once you have dialed into reality, getting away from it is not so easy.

21

Back home from a short excursion into the mountains, I take my studies to the next level. I read several books of current, cutting-edge cosmology. I revisit Stephen Hawking's work, pay close attention as Michio Kaku explains String Theory, and gobble up Dennis Overbye's *Lonely Hearts of the Cosmos*. But the best of the bunch is Kirshner's *The Extravagant Universe*, which makes supernovas, the accelerating cosmos, and dark energy intelligible even to a rank amateur astronomer like myself.

Robert Kirshner is an American astronomer who understands the physics of supernovas as well as anyone does. After working diligently in the field during the 1980s and 90s, he has come to accept the expanding universe as a matter of fact. He knows that both supernovas and cosmic microwave background radiation are critical to understanding the nature of that expansion. In *The Extravagant Universe,* he writes: "The cosmic microwave background (CMB) provides the most direct evidence that the universe had its origin in a hot Big Bang." But the evidence provided by supernovas pulls a very close second.

What exactly is a supernova? As stated clearly at NASA's APOD website, it is "the death explosion of a massive star, resulting in a sharp increase in brightness followed by a gradual fading." The key word here is "massive." How massive? More massive than the Sun to be sure. If a star is massive enough, it begins a more advanced version of *nucleosynthesis* at the end of its hydrogen-burning phase. During this process, a massive star fuses simple atoms into the heavy elements of the universe. When it is finished doing that, its core collapses in a matter of seconds causing the outer layers of the star to blow off in what we call a *supernova*. This event creates a burst of light billions of times brighter than our Sun. That means we can see a supernova when is occurs in a distant galaxy. And there you have it, yet another intergalactic distance marker, as accurate as cepheid variable stars but visible over much greater distances.

"The best candidate for measuring the universe are SN 1a," Kirshner wrote in his book, "The type of supernova that comes from the thermonuclear explosion of a white dwarf." But there's a problem. Supernovas like this occur in any given galaxy only once every hundred years or so. A great deal of observation would be necessary to witness just one. And some powerful tools would be required. Kirshner's team, along with competing teams of astronomers, set to work.

During the early 90s, Kirshner and his colleagues studied the remnants of a supernova that occurred 1987 in the nearby irregular galaxy, Large Magellanic Cloud. That gave them a distance measurement of 165,000 light years between our galaxy and that one – a number that matched cepheid variable measurements. But that wasn't good enough. In order to determine a precise number for the Hubble Constant (H_o), and thus accurately measure the rate of the universe's expansion, they had to find a lot more supernovas in other galaxies. The more distant the galaxies in which they found those supernovas, the better.

During the 1990s, astronomers found dozens of supernovas in distant galaxies. The Hubble Telescope, launched into space in 1990, helped facilitate this. Although mirror defects were discovered in that telescope shortly after its launch, the problem was fixed by 1993. Then astonishingly accurate images of distant galaxies emerged. Kirshner's team made good use of these images. By 1998, they had gathered sufficient information about supernovas to show "that cosmic expansion *had sped up during the last 5 billion years.*"

Meanwhile, scientists were still analyzing the data provided by the Cosmic Background Explorer (COBE), which flew between 1989 and 1996. In 1992, it measured subtle fluctuations in the CMB, giving us some idea what the early universe looked like. And that was the first hard evidence supporting the Big Bang Theory.

What does all this imply? Only that the universe began with a singularity and has been expanding ever since, with the rate of that expansion *increasing* over time. Egads! In order to have a nice, tidy creation story, the universe should end just as it began, collapsing back onto itself in a Big Crunch. From a strictly rational point of view, this makes the most sense. But what we have instead is a universe that began once yet has no apparent end. Welcome to the impossible cosmos.

Setting my books aside one afternoon, I ponder the origin and nature of the universe while listening to a rather obscure CD by Amon Tobin called *Out From Out Where*. I putter about the house doing menial chores as Tobin's jazz electronica ferries my cosmic thoughts to the far shores of plausibility. "Bach in Space" works especially well to this effect, but the next cut better captures the cognitive dissonance that I'm experiencing. Twenty-five hundred of years of cosmology explode in my head with all the force of a type SN 1a supernova. That explosion has blown off the outer layer of reason, leaving the remnant core of my mind to collapse into a black hole of unknowing. No further information is available, so I wallow in existential angst as Tobin's heavy drumbeats batter my brain. By the time "Cosmo Retro Intro Outro" plays, I've given up all hope of understanding the universe in which I exist. I drool, therefore, I am.

Coming home early from work on a particularly dreary autumn day, my wife Judy stumbles into one of my Tobin concerts while I'm preparing dinner. She finds this so-called music annoying as hell. I tell her it suits my mood these days as I wrestle with cosmological incongruities and the endless permutations of the divine. Judy shakes her head. She has had to endure many of outbreaks of wild speculation through the years. But this one takes the cake. Now there is no doubt in her mind that she's married to a madman.

"The universe is wilder than we imagine," Kirshner says, "We keep underestimating how weird it really is." I'll second that. The wildest speculations that philosophers, cosmologists and mystics make about the nature of the universe doesn't come close to the extravagances of reality. And that old bugaboo gravity is sure to keep our heads spinning for many years to come.

Just when it seemed like scientists were on the verge of making sense of the world, black holes were discovered. But "discovery" may not be the best word to use here. Actually, our understanding of black holes began over 200 years ago and it still isn't complete. Rightly so. Black holes are elusive by nature, quite unlike the more conventional stellar objects. After all, they do not emit light.

In the late 1700s, a British scientist named John Michell speculated that there could exist a star with a gravitational field strong enough to prevent light from escaping it. The French astronomer, Pierre-Simon Laplace, made a similar claim in *The System of the World*, but removed this wild speculation from later editions of that book. No doubt his peers warned him that such a notion was too fantastic to be taken seriously. All the same, these "dark stars" lurked in the background of astrophysics for over a hundred years, until Albert Einstein came along with his Theory of Relativity.

According to Einstein's Relativity, gravity is a strong enough force to warp spacetime itself. This results in the bending of light, among other things. Bend light far enough and what happens? It arcs back towards itself, thus disappearing. But that's impossible, isn't it?

As Stephen Hawking later wrote in *A Brief History of Time*, the General Theory of Relativity "predicts that there is a point in the universe where the theory itself breaks down. Such a point is an example of what mathematicians call a singularity." So what is a black hole then? It is a point in spacetime, a singularity, where gravity runs amok.

While traveling to Great Britain in 1928, on a slow boat from his native India, it occurred to Subrahmanyan Chandrasekhar that a star could be massive enough to gravitationally collapse. Chandrasekhar immediately set to work calculating the mass that such a star would have to have in order to do that. The sufficient mass needed for stellar collapse is now known as the Chandrasekhar Limit – roughly 1.4 times the mass of our Sun. A star less massive is simply a white dwarf at the end of its hydrogen burning process. But a stellar mass larger than that results in a supernova explosion with a collapsing core. If the remaining core is less than three times the mass of our Sun, it stabilizes as an extremely dense neutron star. If the core's mass is greater than that, it undergoes a runaway gravitational collapse – a phenomenon better known these days as a black hole.

In the 1950s, the discovery of quasars by radio astronomers blew the lid off conventional notions of distance, luminosity, and the relative power of extragalactic objects. Quasars, or quasi-stellar radio sources, had such great red shifts and were so bright that they had to be very far away and much more powerful than the biggest known galaxies. But that made no sense. Then Fred Hoyle suggested that they might be the result of the gravitational collapse of million-solar-mass stars. In other words, quasars are black holes operating at the galactic level on the very frontier of the visible universe.

The American scientist, John Wheeler, coined the term "black hole" in 1967 to explain strange, dark star phenomena. By then two British astrophysicists – Roger Penrose and Stephen Hawking – had delved deeply into the subject. In 1970 they showed that "according to general relativity, there must be singularity of infinite density and space-time curvature within a black hole." *Infinite* density, of course. Just when it seemed like cosmology couldn't get any stranger...

During the 1970s, astronomers found nearby stars with extremely powerful X ray emissions – far too strong to match the luminosity of the objects from whence they came. Penrose, Hawking and others speculated that such stars were actually binary star systems of a different sort. Usually, a binary star is just two separate stars locked in a gravitational dance around each other. But in the case of Cygnus X-1 and other binaries like it, a regular star is locked in a gravitational dance with an unseen black hole. And from there, the myth of the dark star morphed into its reality.

Nowadays many astrophysicists believe that black holes exist at the center of many galaxies – especially those that are large and well organized, such as spiral and giant elliptical galaxies. As Waller and Hodge stated so clearly in *Galaxies and the Cosmic Frontier*: "Black holes of the galactic variety are like their stellar counterparts, but much bigger." Recently scientists have found evidence suggesting that a giant black hole of this sort exists at the center of our own Milky Way, near Sagittarius A. Could black holes be the most fundamental *organizing* force in the universe?

"We are not quite sure what happens inside a black hole," Stephen Hawking tells us. This has to be the greatest understatement of our time. The *event horizon* is the point-of-no-return boundary surrounding every black hole – an edge beyond which we can have no knowledge. As Hawking pointed out in 1974, black holes leak radiation, thanks to quantum fluctuations that occur along the event horizon, but this information is negligible, really. What leaks out of a black hole is only a tiny fraction of what goes into one. So where does that leave us?

Time and again, cosmology brings us back to the same point: the bizarre aspects of deep space reality. Both secular and religious folk alike long to put the world in a box – to make it behave according to laws, either mechanistic or utterly divine, that cannot be violated. But the cosmos itself defies any simplistic explanation of things. Nothing proves this more than the physics of black holes, where quantum mechanics and relativity meet, where information is lost. The solution to the riddle of gravity and, quite possibly, the nature of the universe itself lies within black holes. Will we ever be able to extract that solution?

As John Wheeler liked to remind himself: "We will first understand how simple the universe is when we understand how strange it is." Simple, yes. Simplistic, no. To know the difference between the two, one must comprehend the role of elegance in design.

An aeronautics engineer once told me that lousy airplane designs are cumbersome and complicated while good ones are elegant. This sounds an awful lot like *Occam's razor* – that rule of thumb which so many scientists and philosophers invoke whenever they're groping for a breakthrough in understanding. Occam's razor states that once a problem has been shaved down to its bare essentials, the simplest explanation is usually the right one. The big question is: How to frame the problem? Here we would be wise to emulate Copernicus, Newton and Einstein, framing our problems in ways that no one else would even consider. Only then can our understanding of the *real* universe arise phoenix-like from the impossible one.

22

October 12th. No moon tonight. As luck has it, the sky is exceptionally clear. I carry my telescope outside right after dinner. On the far side of the Autumnal Equinox now, the days are getting shorter. All the same, it's almost eight o'clock before the sky is dark enough to see the Milky Way, thanks to Daylight Savings Time.

Keenly aware that this may be my last opportunity to wander through the stars before the chill of winter hampers my stargazing, I take in as much of the night sky as I can. I sweep through the constellations much the same way I did a month ago while camped in the mountains. I snap up deep sky objects as if I were on an Easter egg hunt. First I visit familiar nebulas in and around the constellation Sagittarius then I move into Scutum to find the Wild Duck Cluster (M11), a rather busy, open cluster of stars. Suddenly it occurs to me that I should make a list of all that I see, just as birdwatchers do. I'm losing track.

Next I go looking for a couple of planetary nebulas – M57 in Lyra and M27 below Cygnus. I find them both easily enough. M27 is the more impressive of the two. I adjust my focuser ever so slightly as I stare at that object. M27, the Dumbbell Nebula, isn't much to see with my small telescope – just another fuzzy circle. All the same, I'm wowed by the fact that I'm viewing a *planetary nebula.* Similar to a supernova remnant, a planetary nebula is the remnant of a star that has jettisoned its outer layer of gas. I'm not exactly sure what the difference is between the two, but I'm no less awestruck by what is now filling the eyepiece of my telescope. It feels like I'm bearing witness to a great cosmic event.

As always, I turn to Andromeda Galaxy for a quick view. Seeing it with binoculars is sufficient. I've been there enough times to know what it looks like up close. So I move right away to the region between the constellations Andromeda and Triangulum in an attempt to find Triangulum Galaxy (M33). When I think I have a good handle on the configuration of lesser stars in that region, I point my telescope at it. Celestial coordinates verify that I'm in the right spot. I tweak the slow motion cables ever so gently to make that faint object appear. And there it is! M33 emerges ghostlike from the darkness, the faintest galaxy I've located to date. I look away then immediately return to it. I do this again just to be sure of what I'm seeing. At long last, I've found the third spiral galaxy in our Local Group. And with that success I call it a night.

Back inside, I grope for some sense of scale while pondering supernovas and planetary nebulas. It's almost impossible to grasp the magnitude of such events, the formation of galaxies over billions of years, or the evolution of the universe as a whole. Surely I'm not alone in this. When it comes to the cosmos, the disparity between what I *see* and what I *think* is so great that they might as well be two different things. The philosopher and the astronomer use their brains in entirely different ways. Yet it's the same reality. Who is capable of being an observer and an abstract thinker simultaneously?

Cosmologists nowadays are more open to possibilities than they ever have been. They're adding more dimensions to spacetime, talking of multiple universes, twisting the geometry of space into knots, and listening for harmonics. They toy with new models of cosmic order and chaos. The cosmological constant that Einstein dropped from his equations long ago is being reconsidered. So is the rather archaic notion of "ether" – that space itself is a substance. It seems like no theory is too outlandish, no idea too absurd for some cosmologist to entertain.

We've come a long way since the days when Galileo stood before the Italian Inquisition denying the obvious. When the Catholic Church recently admitted that it had made errors during the trial of Galileo nearly four hundred years ago, rational people everywhere laughed long and hard. Talk about too little too late! But reading between the lines, one can see the necessity of such a move. The Catholic Church has to get with the program. Either that or be left in the dust. Will other organized religions do the same?

"Religion will not regain its old power until it can face change in the same spirit as does science," Alfred North Whitehead wrote in *Science and the Modern World*. No doubt many people agree with this, but I see things a bit differently. It seems to me that atheists are conspiring with conventionally religious thinkers to keep the definition of God far too simplistic to have any real meaning in our day and age. Meanwhile most scientists grope for an understanding of the universe while automatically dismissing the possibility of any organizing force beyond the apparent mechanics of the physical world. What's wrong with this picture?

The more I learn, the more skeptical I become. The mounting data on supernovas recently gathered by astronomers points to the same bizarre cosmos suggested by that APOD website that I found on the Internet at the beginning of the year. As Robert Kirshner stated in *The Extravagant Universe* while discussing the data gathered on supernovas: "Combined with the CMB measurements, the measurements point to a universe that is approximately two-thirds dark energy and one-third dark matter." The chart in Kirshner's book shows regular matter wedged between the two – a very thin sliver of the cosmic pie. There's no escaping this conclusion, I suppose. Early in the 21st Century, we now know that we live in a mysterious universe composed mostly of stuff that we cannot see and energy that we do not understand.

In 1933, when an eccentric Swiss astronomer named Fritz Zwicky first started talking about the "missing mass" of galaxies, few scientists took him seriously. But later on they did. It was just a matter of reformulating the problem. "Astronomers no longer call this missing mass as they once did," the American astronomer Vera Rubin wrote in the 1980s, " For it is the light, not the matter, which is missing." This she concluded after years of pioneering work on the nature of galactic halos, where globular clusters appear to be suspended above and below the main disc of spiral galaxies. It turns out that Zwicky's "missing mass" wasn't missing as all. We just can't see it, so now we call it dark matter. And yes, some of that dark matter is stuff like planets, burnt-out stars and the like. But most of it is a subatomic phenomenon with qualities that particle physicists are still trying to define.

As for dark energy, well, that's another issue altogether – one esoteric enough to cause even the most atheistic cosmologist to look over his/her shoulder. Dark energy, we are told, is what made the Big Bang go bang. The physicist Alan Guth has a theory about it. According to Guth's Inflationary Model, "All the momentum of the Big Bang was produced by the gravitational repulsion." Did he say *repulsion*? That's right, an anti-gravitational force at work on a cosmic scale – an outward-pushing *yin* to match gravity's attracting *yang*. If ever there was a time to cross our legs and start chanting mantras, this is it.

Dark matter and dark energy are enough in themselves to cause anyone's head to explode, but the wonders of 21st Century cosmology don't stop there. As the astrophysicist Margaret Geller stated so simply: "Gravity acts to increase the lumpiness of matter in the universe." That we can see in CMB maps of the early universe, of course. There is new empirical data to support this as well. Astronomers are currently mapping the universe at large. The more we learn about the distribution of galaxies, the more we see how the filamentary structure of the universe – how galaxies tend to cluster – reflects the primeval distribution of

CMB. That's hard evidence of the cosmos organizing itself since the Big Bang, as if we didn't already have plenty to consider. What next?

I don't presume to fully understand the nature of things. I feel like a swimmer who has ventured into waters so deep and so vast that all I can do is dog paddle back towards shore. But there are philosophical implications in modern cosmology that anyone with a modicum of intelligence should be able to see. A random universe is about as credible a theory nowadays as the Steady State one was half a century ago. One can believe in randomness if one wants, but the incoming stream of facts weighs heavily against it.

Michio Kaku says it best in *Beyond Einstein*: "We are beginning to realize that nature, at the fundamental level, does not just prefer symmetry in a physical theory, nature demands it." While I'm hesitant to embrace Supersymmetry, String Theory, or any model of the universe that requires dimensions beyond the usual four, I see Kaku's point. For one reason or another, nature wants to organize.

23

Once again the Great Andromeda Galaxy fills the eyepiece of my telescope as I commence yet another night of viewing. It's the middle of November, just a few days past a new moon, and the sky is sufficiently dark and clear. It has taken a while but eventually I have learned when to drag out my telescope and point it skyward, and when to keep it indoors. Good viewing depends upon clarity and light.

Funny how I can't get enough of Andromeda. I keep coming back to it, time and again, even though there's really not much of it that I can see with my small telescope. But this time of year, when Andromeda rides high in the night sky, who can resist? It haunts an otherwise obscure pocket of darkness – a ghostly reminder of what lies beyond the sea of stars that we call the Milky Way. It beckons inquisitive minds, daring us to look deeper into reality, thus abandoning our comfortable and complacent worldviews. In the cloudless chill of a November night, looking at Andromeda instills a profound sense of awe. Only two and a half million light years away, it is practically our next-door neighbor in the greater scheme of things. Yet any vestige of human civilization will be long gone by the time the light emanating from our Sun today reaches alien eyes over there. How then are we to make sense of the cosmos at large?

The Standard Model of the cosmos, which I have only touched upon in this book, is what most astrophysicists embrace these days. After sketching out the Standard Model in his book *The First Three Minutes*, Stephen Weinberg admits that this model "Is not the most satisfying theory imaginable of the origin of the universe." We want the origin and nature of things to be a little less vague than quantum mechanics will allow. We want more logical inevitability than any cosmic soup of subatomic particles is capable of delivering. We long for a Creator, possessing qualities much like our own, saying in a commanding voice: "Let there be Light!" thus commencing all existence with the kind of dramatic flair it deserves. But the Big Bang was nothing like that. The Big Bang occurred in deep silence, at the very threshold of time and space, triggered by a force even more mysterious to us than gravity. There is no making sense of it, really – not during my lifetime, anyhow. As I pack up my telescope and haul it back indoors, this thought weighs heavily upon me.

Others take a tougher stance. "I do not agree with the view that the universe is a mystery," Stephen Hawking once wrote, "Something that one can have intuition about but never fully analyze or comprehend." And that's the kind of attitude a scientist should have, I suppose. But I am not a scientist. I'm a woods wanderer, a scribbler of words, a renegade philosopher, so the prospect of full comprehension seems to me to be the most fantastic of all our illusions. Hats off to

Hawking and all the other scientists working hard to improve our understanding of the cosmos. But a full comprehension of it? Come on now. Get real.

The challenge facing those of us living today is to make as much sense of the world as possible without falling into the prejudices and pitfalls of our predecessors. The great danger is that we might fall back on common sense, which probing inquiries of the cosmos have proven to be wrong time and time again. More than anything else, we need to be flexible when we try to understand the nature of things. We need to be ready to admit the many errors that are embedded in our fixed worldviews as assumptions. After all, Nature with a capital "N" is not so fixed.

"The dance of contingency, of the indeterminable, outwits us all," Loren Eiseley so keenly observed in his book, *The Unexpected Universe*. Before we make any claims about the nature of things, attempt to define God, or assert the role that we play in the grand design, we would be wise to keep this in mind. Whether we like it or not, chaos and order are locked together in a cosmic dance that will probably not end the same way that it began. In other words we live in an impossible cosmos, and clinging to any fixed version of the world – be it religious or secular – is sheer folly.

A year has passed since I first looked to the night sky with the desire burning deep within me to know everything that can be known about the cosmos. It has been a fun ride and I've learned a great deal more science than I ever thought I would, but I've only scratched the surface. I've seen distant galaxies and other nebulous objects with my own eyes and have become quite familiar with a few of them, but am still only a novice astronomer. Truth is, I have wandered in and out of that starry wilderness enough to understand just how vast it is. And that's about all. The cosmos at large is wild beyond my imagination.

"A tamed wilderness will subject itself to man," Loren Eiseley reminds us, "Not so the wilderness beyond the stars or concealed in the infinitesimal world beneath the atom." Some people believe that we are on the verge of knowing all there is to know – everything of practical value, that is. Such is the conceit of every age, I imagine. The most difficult concepts for us grasp are precisely those we are not prepared to see. In this sense, the world we live in will always be wild; the cosmos will always be impossible. Above all else, we should learn how to live with great mystery.

As for the Big Questions, well, I'll keep pondering them even though I don't expect myself or anyone else to hit upon Big Answers anytime soon. I'll keep wondering and wandering wherever I find wilderness – in the heavens above, here on planet Earth, or in my own head. I have little choice, really. It's in my nature to ask questions. It's in the nature of all of us. It's only human to ask questions for which there are no credible answers.

Notes

Quote Page

"In the beginning..." Genesis 1:1, *The Jerusalem Bible* (Doubleday, 1968) p. 5.

"Which pattern..." Originally appeared in Plato's *Timaeus*. Reprinted in *The Book of the Cosmos*, edited by Dennis Richard Danielson (Perseus Publishing, 2000) p. 31-32.

"If you admit the existence..." Originally appeared in *The Guide of the Perplexed,* written by Moses Maimonides in the 12th Century. Reprinted in *The Book of the Cosmos*, p. 84.

"Quantum Mechanics..." This statement originally appeared in a letter written from Albert Einstein to Max Born. Quoted by Michio Kaku in *Beyond Einstein* (Anchor Books, 1995) p. 47.

"If the universe is ... self-contained..." Stephen Hawking, *A Brief History of Time* (Bantam, 1988) p. 141.

Chapter 1

"Mystery generates wonder..." Ursula Goodenough, *The Sacred Depths of Nature* (Oxford University Press, 1998) p.13.

"During the day..." Ken Croswell, *The Universe at Midnight* (The Free Press, 2001) p. xi.

"To take the universe on..." Ursula Goodenough, *The Sacred Depths of Nature*, p. 168.

Chapter 2

"The night sky is the hunting ground..." Chet Raymo, *The Soul of the Night* (Ruminator Books, 1992) p. 40.

"The foregoing generations beheld God..." Ralph Waldo Emerson, *Nature*, facsimile of the first edition (Beacon Press, 1985) p. 5.

"Every poet has trembled..." From *The Journal of Henry David Thoreau* (Peregine Smith Books, 1984) vol. 4, p. 239.

Chapter 3

"Wherever science leaves off..." Sir James Jeans, *Physics and Philosophy* (Dover, 1981) p. 17.

"Giant galaxies..." Croswell, *The Universe at Midnight*, p. 66.

Chapter 4

"All things flow" is a fragment from the writings of Heraclitus, referenced by Robert S. Brumbaugh in his book, *The Philosophers of Greece* (SUNY Press, 1981) p. 45.

"The music of the spheres." Pythagoras, quoted in Brumbaugh's *The Philosophers of Greece*, p. 37.

"That which is created..." From Plato's *Timaeus*, reprinted in *The Book of the Cosmos*, p. 31.

"Most people..." From Aristotle's *On the Heavens*, reprinted in *The Book of the Cosmos*, p. 39.

"Aristarchus of Samos..." Comment by Archimedes reprinted in *The Book of the Cosmos*, p. 44.

Chapter 5

"The most valued facts..." Chet Raymo, *Honey From Stone* (Hungry Mind Press, 1987) p. 151.

"Technology is a mixed blessing." Chet Raymo, *The Path* (Walker Publishing, 2003) p. 125.

Chapter 6

"You cannot understand..." Indries Shah, *Thinkers of the East* (Penguin, 1972) p. 109.

"The earth can have no motion..." Taken from Ptolemy's *Almagest*, reprinted in *The Book of the Cosmos*, p. 72.

Chapter 7

"It is now known..." P. A. Cox, *The Elements* (Oxford Univ. Press, 1990) p. 2.

"Nothing in nature is exhausted..." Ralph Waldo Emerson, *Nature*, p. 52.

My claim that Orion Nebula is "the closest stellar nursery to us" is a paraphrase of "the closest region to us where burgeoning high-mass star formation prevails," which was stated by William H. Waller and Paul W. Hodge in *Galaxies and the Cosmic Frontier* (Harvard Univ. Press, 2003) p. 97.

"There's enough hydrogen, helium and other material..." is a paraphrase of a statement made by Chet Raymo in *The Soul of the Night* (Ruminator Books, 1992) p. 136.

Chapter 8

"This year, humanity learned..." was taken from the Astronomy Picture of the Day website for December 31, 2003 - A Year of Resolving Cosmology, as was the quote: "the universe is composed..."

"Tune a television set ..." is from the article "The Cosmic Symphony," written by Wayne Hu and Martin White, in *Scientific American*, February, 2004, p. 44.

"Every natural fact..." Ralph Waldo Emerson, *Nature*, p. 33.

Chapter 9

"Seeing through a telescope..." Chet Raymo, *The Soul of the Night*, p. 6.

"For Copernicus the motion of the earth..." Thomas S. Kuhn, *The Copernican Revolution* (Harvard University Press, 1957) p. 144.

"The Book of the Revolutions..." Arthur Koestler, *The Sleepwalkers* (Penguin Books, 1989, Arkana edition) p. 194.

"For the earth is not the center..." From *De Revolutionibus Orbium Coelestium* by Nicholas Copernicus, reprinted in *The Book of the Cosmos*, p. 115.

"It seemed an absurd idea." Nicholas Copernicus, reprinted in *The Book of the Cosmos*, p. 107.

"What is it that transforms..." Kuhn, *The Copernican Revolution*, p. 76.

Chapter 10

"When Galileo put down his telescope..." Chet Raymo, *The Soul of the Night*, p. 164.

"The real danger..." Arthur Koestler, *The Sleepwalkers*, p. 465.

"May God forgive Galileo..." is a direct quote from Pope Urban VIII, recounted by Giorgio de Santillana in *The Crime of Galileo* (Time Inc., 1962) p. 235.

Chapter 11

"By the name God..." From Rene Descartes *Meditations*, reprinted in *The Rationalists* (Doubleday, 1974) p. 137.

"The force acting between two bodies..." is Newton's Law of Universal Gravitation, as explained by Charles O. Brass in *The Essentials of Astronomy* (Research and Education Association, 1995) p. 4.

"At the end of the century..." Alexandre Koyré, *From the Closed World to the Infinite Universe* (Johns Hopkins Press, 1968) paperback edition, p. 274.

"For it may be that..." Written by Sir Isaac Newton in *Principia Mathematica* and reprinted in *The Book of the Cosmos,* p. 225.

Chapter 12

"Nature is an infinite sphere ..." Blaise Pascal, *Pensées* (Penguin Books, 1966) p. 89.

"The collision of two galaxies..." Waller and Hodge *Galaxies and the Cosmic Frontier*, p. 191.

"Thus all the suns..." is from Immanuel Kant's *Universal Natural History and Theory of the Heavens*, reprinted in *The Book of the Cosmos*, p. 268.

"Island universes" is a phrase generally associated with the galactic theory of William Herschel, although he preferred the term, "island nebulae." I came upon a direct reference to "island universes" in association with Herschel, in *Widening Horizons* by Zdenek Kopal (Taplinger Publishing, 1971) p. 123.

"Space is not an empirical concept..." Immanuel Kant, *Critique of Pure Reason* (Doubleday, 1966) p. 23.

Chapter 13

"If you know absolute magnitudes..." John Gribbin, *The Birth of Time* (Yale University Press, 2001) p. 89.

"To astronomers of 1885..." Ken Croswell, *The Universe at Midnight* (Free Press, 2001) p. 20.

"Edwin Hubble never really subscribed to any theory..." John Gribbin, *The Birth of Time*, p. 106.

"On October 23, 1923..." Ken Croswell, *The Universe at Midnight*, p. 30.

Chapter 14

"If there really are suns..." Written by H. W. M. Olbers in an astronomy journal and reprinted in *The Book of the Cosmos*, p. 295.

"The velocity-distance relation..." Written by Edwin Hubble in *The Realm of the Nebulae*, reprinted in *The Books of the Cosmos*, p. 400.

"God does not play dice" is a quote by Albert Einstein mentioned in many books on theoretical physics. It appears in Michio Kaku's *Beyond Einstein*, (Anchor Books, 1995) on page 47, and in Stephen Hawking's *A Brief History of Time* (Bantam Books, 1988) on page 56.

Chapter 15

The phrase "was an insufficient foundation..." appears in Albert Einstein's *Relativity* (Crown, 1961) p. 13.

The phrases "to abandon either the principle of relativity or..." and "no empirical data" Einstein, *Relativity*, p. 19.

"Mathematics is the poetry of logic." Paul Davies, *God and the New Physics* (Simon and Schuster, 1983) p. 222.

"A singularity is the nearest thing..." Paul Davies, *God and the New Physics*, p. 55.

"The first principles..." Democritus, reprinted in *The Book of the Cosmos*, p. 25.

"The idea that light..." Michio Kaku, *Beyond Einstein*, p. 38.

"It is difficult to decide..." Banesh Hoffmann, *The Strange Story of the Quantum* (Dover, 1959) p. 177.

"It is not space and time that are basic..." Banesh Hoffmann, *The Strange Story of the Quantum*, p. 196.

Chapter 16

"Here the Reason flies..." is taken from "Eureka: A Prose Poem" by Edgar Allen Poe, reprinted in *The Book of the Cosmos*, p. 308.

"The expansion of the universe..." From an article by George Édouard Lemaître that appeared the journal *Nature*, then reprinted in *The Book of the Cosmos*, p. 409.

"Hubble and Einstein both had thought it was nutty..." Dennis Overbye, *Lonely Hearts of the Cosmos* (HarperCollins, 1991) p. 38.

"Philosophically, the notion of a beginning..." Written by Arthur Eddington in an article for *Nature*, reprinted in *The Book of the Cosmos*, p. 403.

"The big bang idea..." From Fred Hoyle's *The Nature of the Universe*, reprinted in *The Book of the Cosmos*, p. 411.

"Most elements..." P. A. Cox, *The Elements,* p. 91.

Chapter 17

"With the advent of GUTs..." Dennis Overbye, *Lonely Hearts of the Cosmos*, p. 235.

"Quantum uncertainty..." Dennis Overbye, *Lonely Hearts of the Cosmos*, p. 234.

Chapter 18

"All macroscopic existences..." W. T. Stace, *Mysticism and Philosophy* (Tarcher, 1987 reprint) p. 22-23.

"It is God's nature..." taken from *Meister Eckhart: A Modern Translation* (Harper and Row, 1941, 24th printing) p. 243.

Chapter 19

"The eternal silence of these infinite spaces..." Blaise Pascal, *Pensées*, p. 95.

"Indeed, there is a greater nature..." Guy Murchie, *Music of the Spheres* (Dover, 1967) vol. 1, p. 6.

Chapter 20

"Chaos is the inevitable consequence..." Chet Raymo, *The Path*, p. 144.

Chapter 21

"The cosmic microwave background..." Robert Kirshner, *The Extravagant Universe* (Princeton Univ. Press, 2002) p. 116.

The definition of a supernova: "the death explosion of a massive star..." was taken from the glossary of the Astronomy Picture of the Day website.

"The best candidate..." Robert Kirshner, *The Extravagant Universe*, p. 104.

"That cosmic expansion..." Robert Kirshner, *The Extravagant Universe*, p. 221.

"The universe is wilder..." Robert Kirshner, *The Extravagant Universe*, p. 5.

Relativity "predicts that there is a point in the universe..." Stephen Hawking, *A Brief History of Time*, p. 46.

"According to general relativity..." Stephen Hawking, *A Brief History of Time*, p. 88.

"We are not quite sure..." Stephen Hawking, *Black Holes and Baby Universes and Other Essays* (Bantam, 1994) p. 154.

"Black holes of the galactic variety..." Waller and Hodge, *Galaxies and the Cosmic Frontier*, p. 24.

"We will first understand..." Quote by John Wheeler, reprinted in Dennis Overbye's *Lonely Hearts of the Cosmos*, p. 94.

Chapter 22

"Religion will not regain its old power..." Alfred North Whitehead, *Science and the Modern World* (Free Press, 1967) p. 189.

"Combined with CMB measurements..." Robert Kirshner, *The Extravagant Universe*, p. 253.

"Astronomers no longer call this missing mass..." Appeared in a chapter written by Vera Rubin for *Bubbles, Voids and Bumps in Time: The New Cosmology*, edited by James Cornell (Cambridge Univ. Press, 1992 reprint) p. 73.

"All the momentum of the Big Bang..." Appeared in a chapter written by Alan Guth for *Bubbles, Voids and Bumps in Time: The New Cosmology*, p. 135.

"Gravity acts to increase the lumpiness..." Appeared in a chapter written by Margaret Geller for *Bubbles, Voids and Bumps in Time: The New Cosmology*, p. 67.

"We are beginning to realize..." Michio Kaku, *Beyond Einstein*, p. 100.

Chapter 23

"The standard model ... is not the most satisfying theory..."
Written by Stephen Weinberg in *The First Three Minutes*,
reprinted in *The Book of the Cosmos*, p. 436 .

"I do not agree with the view..." Stephen Hawking, *Black Holes
and Baby Universes and Other Essays*, p. viii.

"The dance of contingency..." Loren Eiseley, *The Unexpected
Universe* (Harcourt Brace Jovanovich, 1969) p. 77.

"A tamed wilderness..." Loren Eiseley, *The Unexpected Universe*,
p. 42.

About the Author

Walt McLaughlin received a degree in philosophy from Ohio University in 1977 and has been wondering, wandering and writing ever since. He has a dozen books in print, including a narrative about his immersion in the Alaskan bush, *Arguing with the Wind*, and one about hiking Vermont's Long Trail, *Forest under my Fingernails*. He is also the force behind a small press called Wood Thrush Books, and has selected and published the works of several 19th-century writers including *The Laws of Nature: Excerpts from the Writings of Ralph Waldo Emerson*. He lives in Saint Albans, Vermont with his wife, Judy.

For more information about Walt's books, visit the WTB website: **www.woodthrushbooks.com**

Go to **www.facebook.com\WaltMcLaughlin** to check out his Facebook page, or read his regularly posted blogs at **www.woodswanderer.com**

Made in the USA
Monee, IL
18 September 2022

14237566R00114